Whom Shall I Fear

Will Mara's new faith remain strong despite the
ravages of war and her family's unbelief?

Ann Vitorovich

Pacific Press® Publishing Association
Nampa, Idaho
Oshawa, Ontario, Canada
www.pacificpress.com

Designed by Eucaris L. Galicia
Cover art by James Converse

Additional copies of this book are available by calling toll free
1-800-765-6955 or by visiting www.adventistbookcenter.com

Scripture quotations in this book are from the King James Version.

Library of Congress Cataloging-in-Publication Data

Vitorovich, Ann, 1933-
Whom shall I fear: will Mara's new faith remain strong despite the ravages of
war and her family's unbelief? / Ann Vitorovich.
        p. cm.
ISBN: 0-8163-2129-9
ISBN13: 9780816321292
1. Vitorovich, Mara. 2. Seventh-day Adventists converts—Yugoslavia—
Biography. I. Title.

BX6189.V58V59 2006
286.7092—dc22
        [B]
2005056626

06 07 08 09 10 · 5 4 3 2 1

Contents

Dedication

To Mara's grandchildren, great-grandchildren,
and great-great grandchildren.
May her life always be their inspiration.

Leka: Jovan, Pavle, Petar, Olgica, Josif, Boźidar, Vlada, Rada, Marko,
        Amaris, Alexis, Sara.

Nata: Jovica.

Voja: George.

Cveja: Danny, Maria, John, Lindsay, Kelsey, Jackson, Ethan.

Main Characters

Mara [Mä' rä]   wife of Ilija and mother of Leka, Nata, Vera, Voja, and Cveja
Ilija [I' lē - yä]   Mara's second husband and father of Nata, Vera, Voja, and Cveja
Leka [Le' kä]   Mara's daughter from her first marriage
Nata [Nä' tä]   Mara and Ilija's oldest daughter
  Natalija [Nä - tä' lyä]
Vera [Ver' ä]   Mara and Ilija's third daughter (their second daughter, Desa,
                  died in infancy)
Voja [Vô' yä]   Mara and Ilija's older twin son
  Vojislav [Vô' yi - släv]
Cveja [Tsve' yä]   Mara and Ilija's younger twin son
  Svetozar [Sve' tô - zär]
Milorad [Mi' lô - räd]
Mihajlo [Mi - hy' lô] Ilija's three brothers
Milosav [Mi' lô - säv]
Jovan [Yô' vän]   father of Ilija, Milorad, Mihajlo, and Milosav
Mladen [Mlä' den]
Petar [Pe' tär]   Mara's two brothers
Živan [Zhi' vän]   Leka's husband
Micá [Mi' chä]   Nata's husband
Lila [Li' lä]   wife of Mihajlo, Ilija's brother
Petra [Pe' trä]   wife of Milorad, Ilija's brother
Živana [Zhi - vä' nä] wife of one of Milorad's sons
Branko [Brän' kô]   younger son of Mihajlo
Marija [Mä' - rē - yä] wife of Mladen, Mara's older brother
Prota Mihajlo
  [*Prô' tä* Mi - hy' lô]Orthodox priest in the town of Glušci
Johann [Yô' hän]   chief mechanic employed by the Vitorovich family
Mila [Mi' lä]   woman who gives Bible studies to Mara

1
A Shot in the Night

Mara sat fully clothed beside the window, peering into the black night. The kerosene lamp on the table beside her cast a soft glow over her fair face, highlighting her chin and high cheekbones. At her feet, on the parquet floor, lay a small black suitcase. And on a feather bed, next to her own, lay Leka, sound asleep.

Getting up, Mara eased the casement window open slightly, cocked her head, and listened. In the stillness outside, she could hear only the sound of the wind rustling the trees in the orchard and whispering around the eaves of the house. Inside, all was quiet; the rest of the family already slept.

A gust of cold air rushed in, flickering the lamplight and sending her shadow dancing on the white plastered wall. She held her coat closer and returned to her chair. Reaching into her coat pocket, she pulled out the watch her father had given her years before and held it toward the light—9:30. *It won't be long now,* she told herself, a smile of anticipation playing on her lips.

Mara had lost her husband early in World War I when Austria-Hungary invaded Serbia which had been freed from the Turks only two years earlier. Eight months pregnant and with a two-year-old daughter at the time, she and her in-laws had fled from the chaos and fighting that erupted around them and had joined the exodus of terrified civilians fleeing south for their lives. Somewhere along the way, she had given birth to a son. He died three weeks later in a typhus epidemic.

Five years ago now. Five years, she mused. *Twenty-eight is too young to be a widow.* The Great War had ended just the year before. It was November 1919 now.

"You should meet my cousin, Ilija," Gavra had suggested every time he saw Mara on his visits to his wife's family who lived in Mara's village. Gavra and Ilija lived in the nearby village of Glušci. "He's tall, good-looking. Wears a field-gray Austrian officer's tunic without its military markings. Makes him look distinguished, like a captain."

"An Austrian uniform? But why?" she had asked, perplexed.

"He got it in Budapest to wear home when the war ended. After four years as a prisoner of war there, his clothes had worn out. He still wears it on occasion. So what do you think, Mara?"

"Well, all right, Gavra. I'll meet this relative of yours," Mara had finally agreed. "But my in-laws must not know. Leka is their son's only child, you know, and they wouldn't want me to leave with her."

"Good. I'll arrange it," Gavra replied. "When?"

"Two weeks from now our church is having its *Slava* celebration. There will be a crowd and a lot of activity, so my meeting your cousin shouldn't attract notice."

"That sounds good," Gavra had replied and left.

When the saint's day came, the day of the *Slava,* the church grounds teemed with activity. Sweet sounds of violins and savory odors of roasting meats floated on the air. Mara remembered it well. There she was, talking with Gavra, when she turned her head and saw him—the tall stranger striding toward them. *So handsome he is,* Mara had thought, *with his dark handlebar mustache and wearing black boots and an Austrian tunic.*

"So you are Mara," Ilija had said, towering over her, his gaze warm. Mara could feel the color rising in her cheeks now as it had then. *When I looked in his face and saw those deep-set dark eyes, that was it.* Their eyes locked, and she was smitten.

Dark eyes always drew Mara's notice. Her own were sky-blue and large and beautiful—but she didn't think so.

Has it been only three months since we met? Only three months? she asked herself. She had met him only a few times, always with others around, and now here she was, waiting for him to wisk her away. But it felt so right. *He's kind, has a fine sense of humor, and he comes from a good family,* she told herself. *When he proposed, I had to say yes.*

"I've met a man who wants to marry me," Mara had confided to her mother-in-law after gathering up her courage. "I hope you understand."

"I do, my daughter. I know we can't hold you here forever. It's time you made a life for yourself. Of course, your father-in-law won't be happy. I won't say anything to him until after you're gone. But, could you leave Leka here—just for a little while?"

"Well, just for a while," Mara had agreed.

Leka is in good hands, she assured herself now, her gaze drifting to her sleeping daughter. She arose, walked to the bed, and brushed her hand gently over Leka's brown head. "Sleep, my lamb, my pet. I must leave, but I won't be far away. I'll see you soon," she whispered. Returning to her chair, she pulled out her watch again. *Only ten minutes to go. Ilija is always punctual. He'll be here soon.* Her heart started to race.

How much do I really know about this man? she suddenly asked herself. Her chest tightened. She reviewed the things Gavra had told her. "Ilija has two living brothers, Milorad and Mihajlo. Milosav, the youngest, had died in the fighting on the very last day of the war. Milorad had served in the King's personal guard. The brothers' families and parents survived, but Ilija lost his wife and son from typhus." *That's one thing we have in common, our loss. The family has a large farm, and they're well respected. I wonder how it'll be.* She sighed. *I guess I'll soon find out.*

Crack! A rifle shot suddenly exploded in the night, startling her out of her reverie. *That's it! The signal!* She jumped up, pushed the window fully open, and tossed her bag to the ground. Quickly, she climbed through the window and then hurried toward the wooden fence separating the house from the road. On the other side she could hear a horse snort and the stamp of its hoof. Opening the gate, she stepped onto the street, breathless. A beautiful black fiacre coach drawn by two midnight-black horses stood waiting. She could barely see it in the dark, except for the movement of the horses and reflection of moonlight on the lacquered finish of the sides of the coach. Beside it, Ilija stood waiting for her.

He took her bag and helped her in. Gavra and another friend had accompanied him. Mara sat beside Ilija as they rode the twelve miles to Glušci, where Ilija's parents welcomed her into their home.

The next day a traditional ceremony in the Glušci Orthodox Church united Mara and Ilija in marriage. *Prota* Mihajlo, the local priest, officiated. Mara's new extended family and a few of their friends attended, with Gavra serving as the best man.

When Mara arrived, the town was still in the throes of rebuilding from the war. Ilija showed her around the family's *zadruga* where the extended family lived, worked together, and owned property jointly.

"I saw a lot of damaged buildings in the village," Mara remarked.

"Glušci was in the path of the Austrian army's main advance. When Milorad and Mihajlo returned, they found the village razed to the ground and the family sleeping on straw in a burned-out barn and horse stall. I didn't get home for another four months. The railroads weren't functioning, and I had to walk most of the way." Ilija explained. "Half our buildings are rebuilt now. But a lot of people are still living in straw-covered huts while they rebuild as they are able to afford it."

Mara could only shake her head at the tragedy and suffering of war. "My village didn't suffer as much," she told him. "Most of the damage has already been repaired.

"Why are the fields so . . . so wavy?" Mara asked, surveying the land beyond the buildings as they continued to walk.

"You should have seen them before. They were all dug up into trenches where the battles were fought. We've pretty much leveled them out again now."

Ilija led Mara to a particularly large, but scarred and charred, apple tree not far away. "My father buried the women's gold ducats, their dowries, at the foot of this tree before they fled. Luckily, they were still there when the family returned."

Not long after the marriage, Ilija's father, Jovan, proposed building a grain mill. "We need to have some kind of industry besides farming," he said. As the patriarch of the family, he was head of the *zadruga*.

"We could cash in our ducats," one of the women offered. The others agreed. And with Mara's ducats (which her former in-laws had returned) added to the family's treasury, there were now more than 500 gold ducats—enough to proceed with their plans.

Brick makers, hired to produce the bricks for the mill, discovered deep deposits of quality clay in a section of the family's land. So the family decided to build a brick factory as well and hire the brick makers on a yearly basis as a second business.

The first bricks, made of clay and chopped straw baked for three days in a make-shift kiln, provided bricks to build the brick factory. After its completion, the brick factory produced fired bricks to construct the grain mill—as well as more bricks to sell. Ilija ordered grinding stones, belts, and a steam-powered motor for the grain mill from Prague. These arrived by rail at the nearest train station eight miles away and then made the rest of the journey to their new home on a cart pulled by four of the family's strongest oxen.

People flocked to the Vitorovich compound from miles around to watch the buildings go up. These were the first businesses in the region to be built after the war, at a time when many people still struggled to survive.

When Mara arrived, Milorad, the oldest and tallest of the brothers, already had four sons. Mihajlo had a daughter and a son, and Milosav's widow had a son. Mara and Ilija were starting over.

A little more than a year after her marriage, Mara presented Ilija with their first child, a girl they named Natalija, or Nata for short. She had brown hair and hazel eyes. Four years later, Desa arrived, a daughter who died of pneumonia while still a toddler. Then three years later, another daughter, named Vera, raven-haired and dark-eyed, made her debut. Meanwhile, Mihajlo's wife had given him a second son.

The fact that she was the only woman in her new extended family who had not borne a son marred Mara's happiness. As time went on, she grieved. *Am I never to give Ilija the son he so much desires? We've both lost our boys. Daughters marry and leave home, but sons remain with their parents. Dear God, am I cursed? Is it my destiny to never to have another son?*

2
1929

In the year 1929, several things happened. The country in which Mara and Ilija lived—established after the disintegration of the Austro-Hungarian Empire and named the Kingdom of Serbs, Croats, and Slovenes—was renamed the Kingdom of Yugoslavia. Jovan died unexpectedly. Nata turned nine, and Vera, two. Ilija made plans to build a new house for his family. Bojana, the largest of the family's cows, calved twins for the first time. And, most important of all, to Mara, she was pregnant again at thirty-eight years of age.

"This time it'll be a boy," the midwives predicted, sending Mara's hopes soaring. *This pregnancy feels decidedly different,* she would tell herself, feeling the frequent kicks, jolts, and thumps. *Please, God, may the midwives be right!* she prayed.

Though tiring easily, Mara did not let pregnancy keep her from doing her work or from faithfully attending liturgy every Sunday. Dressed in her best hat and home-sewn maternity dress, she continued to walk the three miles to the Orthodox church at the other end of Glušci. There she lit candles, recited the Lord's Prayer, and read prayers out of the prayer book before icons of the saints, while her heart ached for a son.

"Good morning, Mara," villagers along the way greeted her. Most of them, as well as the rest of her family, were Orthodox Serbs, but few attended church regularly, most only on special feast days or their family's *Slava.*

"Mara, your tummy precedes you into the room," Ilija joked as she expanded. He ordered a special belt to support her growing belly so that she could get around.

One morning she called out to Ilija. "Help me up, Ilija. I can't get out of bed!" Thereafter, he helped her up each morning. During the last two months of her pregnancy, he engaged two midwives to keep close watch on her wherever she went.

Until now, Ilija and Mara and their children had lived in three large bedrooms in the original house that was attached to the communal kitchen and dining hall. It was there the extended family spent their time when not working and where they ate their meals. Individual houses were used primarily for sleeping. During the busy season, when the family fed two meals a day to sixty or more farm and factory workers, they ate at tables set outside in the courtyard under the trees.

In recent years, Milorad had built an additional house for his family with several bedrooms because three of his sons were married and had children. Now it was Ilija's turn to expand.

"Mara, I want to build a house like the Jewish homes I saw in Budapest," he said one day. "I have a lot of ideas."

So Ilija sketched out a plan. The house had thick walls made of bricks from their factory and a roof of flat red-clay tiles. The entrance consisted of a pair of tall exterior doors set flush with the outside wall, opening out like shutters, and a second pair of decorative paneled doors set flush with the inside wall and opening inward. An attractive transom extended above the inner doors. Six large, double casement windows looked out on the road, with wooden shutters on the outside.

Local laborers would put up the building, assisted by Ilija and his brothers; a local cabinetmaker and his crew would fabricate the woodwork. All the family's houses were entered from the courtyard. Before long, construction began.

By this time, the town of Glušci had been rebuilt and enlarged; the road through town was paved with packed gravel. No visible marks of the war remained. But wars always leave scars. Long after the fighting ends, open wounds linger.

The land owned by Ilija's family's *zadruga* now included 250 acres. His great, great grandfather had purchased the first piece of land at the turn of the nineteenth century when he and his brother had fled with their families from Turkish-occupied Bosnia to the other side of the Drina River, where the Serbs had achieved a measure of independence from the Turks. They had settled outside the village of Glušci, where there was an abundance of fertile black soil.

Besides land, the family now owned ten horses (eight for work and two for show), ten Swiss cows, six oxen, one huge stud bull named Bulko, sixty sheep, one hundred pigs, four long wagons used for hauling, two buggies, two single horse-drawn carriages, and two luxury fiacre coaches reserved for special occasions and drawn by the two show horses.

Ilija had charge of the grain mill; Mihajlo, the farm, orchard, and saw mill; and Milorad, as headman, took care of the overall functioning of the *zadruga*. The women and older children shared a variety of chores—milking cows, feeding animals, caring for children, cooking, and baking. The family's businesses thrived, and before long, farm machinery drawn by horses for sowing and harvesting replaced scythes and hand labor.

One morning in early September, Mara, her sister-in-law, Lila, and her niece, Živana, were working in the field near the grain mill, beating and combing soaked hemp stems, when Mara doubled over. "It's time!" she called out.

"Bring both our satchels!" one of the midwives shouted to the other, as the women led Mara into the original house, where one of the rooms had been set up for the birth. The new house was still under construction.

While Mara rested, the midwives called out orders. "Boil some water! Get some clean white sheets!" Lila and Živana scurried about to help.

One midwife spread a rubber pad on the bed and the white sheets Lila had brought for Mara to lie on, then prepared her for delivery. Mara's contractions quickened, and her delivery progressed rapidly.

"Push, Mara! Push!" the women urged. Soon the head of the child showed. A few minutes later a lusty wail pierced the still morning air.

"It's a boy, Mara! It's a boy!" The women chorused as the midwife held the baby up. She tied and cut off the cord, cleaned up the baby, wrapped him in a cotton blanket, and presented him to his mother.

"Mara," she said, smiling, "See! We were right!" Mara's face glowed. The whole delivery had taken less than an hour. "Now you can rest." She lay the baby next to the bed in an ornate wooden cradle crafted by the local cabinetmaker. Her work done, the midwife ran out of the house toward the grain mill, shouting, "Ilija! Ilija! You have a son! Mara gave birth to a boy!"

Inside the grain mill, an ecstatic Ilija heard the announcement. Workers and customers cheered. The sounds of celebration floated back to the house and to Mara's happy ears.

Meanwhile, Mara started contracting again. "There's another one coming!" the women cried. The midwives prepared for a second birth. Lila dashed out for more sheets, and Živana ran to get her daughter's cradle in which to place the unexpected infant.

Ten minutes after the first birth, another wail rang out. "It's another boy!" the women screamed. "Mara, you have twin boys!"

"Oh, Lord, I've waited so long, and now You've given me two sons. My cup overflows!" she prayed aloud.

After cleaning up and placing the second baby in the borrowed cradle, the second midwife rushed out of the house, shouting as loud as her lungs allowed, "Ilija! Ilija! You have another son. Mara has given birth to twin boys!"

Inside the mill a thunderous roar arose, engulfing the jubilant father in congratulations. Everything stopped, and celebration filled the air. "Long live the twins!" the men's shouts carried into the house.

Resting blissfully on the bed with her sleeping sons within reach on either side, lying in the crib and borrowed cradle, Mara's heart thrilled with gratitude and praise. When Ilija visited later, proudly viewing his sons, he joked, "Mara, you've given me a litter! No wonder you were so big!"

"They weigh over seven pounds each," one of the midwives offered. Ilija immediately sent word for a new crib to be made large enough to accommodate both baby boys.

Eight days later, *Prota* Mihajlo, the priest, came to the house at Ilija's invitation to baptize the boys in the Orthodox manner and to give them the Christian names the parents and godfather had agreed upon.

In no time, the carpenter delivered a beautiful wooden crib painted white and twice the size of the first. One side could be lowered and raised. The twins had begun life together in the same womb. Now they would share the same crib.

Word quickly spread. Friends and neighbors dropped by to admire the boys and see their unusual crib. Everyone thought it a wonder that Mara at age thirty-eight and Ilija at forty should have twins when there were none on either side of the family and no identical twins in the whole area.

One day several strange faces showed up at the door. "Yes?" Mara said. "Do I know you?"

"We came from another village. We heard about the twins and wanted to see them for ourselves!" they confessed. The happy mother obliged.

With two healthy boys, Mara's cup overflowed. God was on His throne. All was well in her world. Little did she know what the next year would bring.

3
Johann's Strange Words

"Cveja seems plumper than Voja. Can you see that?" Mara asked one of the midwives a couple of weeks later.

"Do you nurse them always at the same breast?"

"Yes, Voja on the right—he's first born—and Cveja on the left. They seem to get hungry at the same time, so I feed them together."

"Try switching breasts occasionally," the midwife suggested. "Some people say the left breast has more milk."

But the first time Mara tried putting Cveja at the right breast instead of Voja, Voja reached out his little hand and pushed his brother's mouth away. Mara thought he was playing. But when Cveja resumed nursing, Voja did it again. This time Cveja cried.

"Now, stop that!" Mara scolded Voja. But Voja did not stop. He looked Mara in the eye and did it once more.

"No, no, no!" She flicked her finger gently at his nose. He winced, but the behavior stopped. Apparently, despite their identical genetic inheritance, the different personalities of her twins were beginning to emerge. Every week after that, Mara switched the boys' nursing positions, and they flourished equally.

Within a few weeks, Mara had recuperated sufficiently from childbirth to resume some of her work duties but she continued to wear a belt around her abdomen. She could leave her sleeping twins secure in their crib while working in the kitchen nearby. They still lived in the original house, and someone was always close enough to look in on the boys.

One Sunday, Mara made arrangements with one of her sisters-in-law and prepared to make her first trip to church since the birth of the twins. As she walked in her Sunday best down the steps of her house toward the gate, a familiar voice accosted her from behind. "Mara, Mara, foolish Mara, you should have gone to church yesterday. Today is the first day of the week. Yesterday was the Sabbath."

Startled, Mara whirled around to see Johann, the family's chief mechanic, coming toward her, smiling. But Mara wore no smile for Johann this morning—only a look of disbelief. Stunned by his statement, her joy melted like spring ice. Standing before her, his words and his form cast a shadow across her path.

"Johann, you speak strange words." She drew the large wrapped bundle she was carrying closer under her arm, moved past him through the gate, and into the road. "I can't be late." Her words trailed behind.

Standing at the gate, Johann watched Mara's short, stocky frame grow smaller as she proceeded down the road in long strides. "I'm sorry, Mara. I see I've upset you," he said to himself. "But I've remained silent for so long." Shaking his head, he turned his steps toward the grain mill.

The rays of the morning sun followed Mara's feet over the grassy path that skirted the road through town. As she plodded along, the bundle under her arm grew cumbersome, and she shifted it absentmindedly. All the while, like a phonograph needle stuck in a groove, her mind replayed Johann's words: *"You should have gone to church yesterday. Today's the first day of the week. Yesterday was the Sabbath."* Shaking her head as if to shake off his words, she challenged them in her mind. *How could Johann say such a thing? What's gotten into him, anyway?*

A rabbit hopped across her path and skittered into the bushes. Though autumn's cooler days were creeping in, clumps of yellow wild flowers still smiled from the sides of the road. On a branch somewhere above her head a blue bird hit a high note, and the air burst into melody. Gradually Mara's indignation subsided, but in its place a strange uneasiness surfaced. *Could Johann possibly be right? Have I been worshiping God on the wrong day? How could that be? Don't all Christians go to church on Sunday?* Her mind whirled with confusion.

On the level landscape before her rose the outline of a chalk-white stucco church of Byzantine architecture with three cupolas. An elaborate, gold-plated Byzantine cross atop the largest cupola in the center glistened and sparkled in the sun. Like a sentinel welcoming a weary traveler, the familiar sight warmed Mara's heart.

"Good morning, Mara," a deep melodious voice greeted her. She turned from her prayers and the candles she was lighting in the narthex of the church to see a tall, ample figure in black flowing robes approaching. The priest wore a black *kamilavka* cap on his gray head and an enormous silver Byzantine cross that dangled from a long chain around his neck. A smile played hide-and-seek between his gray mustache and full gray beard that parted in the middle and hung down his chest.

"*Prota* Mihajlo, I brought a gift for the church," Mara exclaimed joyfully. She reached down to unwrap the cloth covering on her package and spread out the colorful tapestry on the wood floor. "I've been weaving this over the past months of my pregnancy while the family slept. It's my gift to the church. A token of my gratitude to God for the sons He gave me. I sheared and dyed the wool myself."

"Magnificent!" *Prota* Mihajlo uttered in delight, surveying her work. "You are most generous, Mara." He smiled down at her approvingly. "Now with your permission, we will sell this tapestry to raise funds to complete the *ikonostas*. A few more decorative icons will make the altar screen beautiful."

Mara nodded in agreement, her cherubic face beaming.

Taking her hand in both of his, the priest shook it enthusiastically, then bent down, gathered up the tapestry, and made his way with the bundle through the nave toward the altar. His robes flapped behind him with each step.

When Mara walked home after liturgy, the sweet smell of incense lingered in her nostrils, and the priest's monotonous singsong still echoed in her ears. But other sounds, less pleasing and comforting, tumbled about in her mind as well. Johann's words troubled her spirit.

Arriving home, Mara found the kitchen astir with preparations for lunch. "Hi, Lila," Mara greeted her sister-in-law as she entered.

"No day laborers today," said Lila, who had charge of the kitchen this week. "The grain mill is down for repairs. There are just the three permanent workers who live here, not to mention the family. Their twenty-six hungry mouths need to be fed."

As Mara busied herself to help, the events of the morning receded to the back of her mind. The door soon opened, and hungry men and children drifted in and seated themselves at two long tables.

From the kitchen, Mara watched Johann stroll in and sit down on the bench across from Ilija. Workers did not customarily eat at the same table with family members, but Johann was an exception.

Having placed steaming platters of food on the tables, the women sat beside their husbands. Then Milorad stood up. The others followed. He recited aloud the Lord's Prayer, crossing himself in the Orthodox manner. The others did the same. "Amen," they chorused.

Once seated, Ilija and Johann plunged into a conversation about a broken part on the mill motor. Mara picked at her food, waiting for an opportunity to speak. The morning's incident, now revived in her mind, spawned many questions.

Between mouthfuls, she glanced across the table at Johann, pursing her lips and thinking. *How much do I really know about Johann? Only that he crossed the Sava River ten years ago and that he's worked for our family ever since. That he's a Volksdeutscher* [comes from a German background], *is a good worker, and that he married a local girl.*

Catching a momentary lull in the conversation, Mara quickly interjected, "Johann, I have to ask you about this morning. What you said troubles me." Her voice sounded earnest.

Ilija turned toward Mara with curious ears, but continued eating.

Johann replied, "I never told you about my background." He took a few bites and laid his fork on his plate. "I come from a devout Roman Catholic family. My father owned a heavy machinery repair shop in Banat. That's where I learned my trade. But my father's dream for me was that I become a priest."

Johann paused and bit his lip. "I went to the monastery and finished my studies, but before taking my vows, I left." His eyes glossed over as he looked past Mara and the roomful of people. Then clearing his throat, he turned back to Mara. "My parents were devastated when I told them. That's when I left home to start a new life here."

"What happened, Johann? Can you tell me? Why didn't you take your vows?" Mara asked, concerned.

"To tell you the truth, Mara, I discovered that my church changed God's Ten Commandment law. In effect, it vetoed God. It cut out the second commandment and split the tenth in two." He paused. "It also changed the fourth commandment, switching the Bible Sabbath from the seventh day of the week to the first day. That's what I meant this morning."

Mara frowned, her face full of question marks. "I don't understand. Isn't Sunday the Christian Sabbath?"

Johann shook his head. "Sunday is a pagan day, a day dedicated to sun worship. Saturday is a memorial of God's creative power. God blessed and made the seventh day holy. Nobody can make that claim for Sunday." He fiddled with his fork. "When the Eastern Church broke away from Rome, back in the eleventh century, it took Sunday worship with it along with other unbiblical traditions. But for a long time the Eastern Church kept both days. No, Mara, Sunday is not a worship day in the Bible. No man can make holy what God has not blessed."

Mara sat in dumb silence, her eyes large, lines etching her forehead. *Have I been displeasing God by worshiping on a pagan day?* Johann met her steady gaze.

"If you really want to know what God says, Mara, go see Mila. You know her. Her husband shoes your horses. She has a Bible." Noticing her distress, he added, "Maybe I shouldn't have said anything." He started to stand. "The real question is not so much which church or which day. It's what authority is behind them, whom we obey—God or man."

Excusing himself, Johann climbed over the bench and walked across the room and out the door. Mara sat still and uncertain.

4
In Search of Answers

Unlatching the gate, Mara walked past the blacksmith shop of Mila's husband. She continued through the courtyard and approached the two-room stucco house in back where the couple lived. Leaving the twins in the care of her sisters-in-law, she had walked the mile from her village to the adjacent town of Uzveće, to see Mila.

Am I doing right? What will Mila tell me? she wondered. Rumors said that Mila belonged to a group called Sabbatarians. Mara wasn't sure what they believed, but Johann said Mila had a Bible, and Mara had to find out what it said.

"Come in, Mara. Come in," Mila welcomed her at her kitchen door. "What brings you here?" Sunlight streamed through two small windows, leaving patches of light on the swept dirt floor. Sitting at the table across from Mila, Mara related her experience with Johann.

"And that's why I came, Mila," Mara wound up her tale. "Johann said you have a Bible. I need to know what it says about the Sabbath."

"God's blessings be on you, Mara," Mila replied, the smile on her face widening. "I'd be happy to study with you. Can you come back Saturday afternoon?"

"Next Saturday? Well, yes . . . but I hoped you could talk with me today. I have so many questions."

"OK, Mara. You want to know about the Sabbath. Let me tell you something more important first. Something at the heart of the Bible."

"What's that?" Mara inquired.

"It's about God's plan to save sinners, the great controversy between good and evil, God and the devil. That is what the Bible is all about. It explains what's wrong with this world. We all need to understand that."

"OK, Mila, tell me everything."

Mila sat back and began. "The Bible says that in the beginning, God made a perfect world and two perfect people. He put Adam and Eve in the Garden of Eden with the tree of life in the middle. Everything was theirs to enjoy—except one tree, the tree of the knowledge of good and evil. God told them that if they ate its fruit, they would die. It was a simple test of their obedience."

Mara leaned forward, listening closely.

"But the devil lied to Eve through a serpent. He was once the greatest angel in heaven, but he rebelled and deceived one-third of the angels and became Satan, the enemy of God. God had to cast him and his followers out of heaven. The devil told Eve she would not die if she ate the forbidden fruit, that instead, she would become like God. He lied, and Eve believed him. Think of it, Mara. God gave Adam and Eve everything, and the devil gave them nothing. Yet they believed the devil—not God. That was their sin. And that was the beginning of all this world's troubles."

Mara sat riveted in her seat. Mila was relating the story in words she could understand.

"As soon as Adam and Eve sinned, their nature and their world changed. God came walking in the Garden like before, but this time they hid. They felt afraid and ashamed and awfully guilty. Not happy like before. And you know, Mara," Mila waved her finger, "people have been hiding like that from God ever since. That old devil still lies and deceives.

"God called to Adam. Of course He knew what had happened. Adam blamed the woman for his sin and also God who gave her to him; Eve blamed the serpent that God had made. People have been doing that, too, ever since—blaming God. Now, God still loved Adam and Eve, but because of their sin, they had to leave the Garden and they would one day die."

Mila shifted in her seat and sipped some water. She had placed two glasses on the table with a jar of cherry preserves and two teaspoons. Mara sat upright, still in the same position. Her water glass remained untouched.

She was drinking in Mila's words and felt satisfied. Mila continued.

"God promised Adam and Eve a Savior and told them they had to kill a lamb. It represented Jesus, the Messiah, who would come to take their punishment so they could one day live forever. That was hard. The animals were their pets. God wanted them to understand how terrible sin is. In sacrificing the lamb they showed their faith. God's Word is eternal. His law cannot be changed. That's why Jesus had to die. Do you understand, Mara?"

"Yes, Mila, go on."

"Because of their sin, all their children were born into sin, like us. We are not happy until we make our peace with God. Pretty soon the world filled up with people who turned against God and became very wicked. So God sent the Flood. But He told Noah to build an ark to save all those who believed his message. How sad that only the animals came! In order to save the human race, God had to destroy those who were evil before they destroyed everything that was good. Only Noah and his family believed and went into the ark."

Mara's face lit up. "It always bothered me that God would destroy the world, but I understand now. God was actually saving the world. It's like when I remove a rotten apple from a bushel to keep it from rotting the rest, isn't it?"

"Exactly, Mara. That's very good." Mila's voice took on more energy as she continued. "Pretty soon the population of the world increased again, and God raised up the Jewish nation to be His chosen people, to tell other nations about the true God and His law. That was their mission. Other nations worshiped idols, the sun, and animals, but the Jews worshiped the Creator God. They made blood sacrifices for their sins to show their faith in the coming Messiah. But the Jews misunderstood the prophecies. When Jesus came, they didn't recognize Him. Only a few believed." Mila paused. "That's how it's always been, Mara. Only a few believe. We can't follow the crowds. They're usually wrong."

Mara was sitting on the edge of her seat, barely breathing.

"Jesus did only good, but wicked people nailed Him to the cross, and He died. On the third day He came out of the grave. Later He went to heaven. The disciples saw Him. Before He went, He promised to come back one day to take them to their heavenly home where they would live forever. There is nothing we can do to earn heaven, you know. We can never be good enough. Jesus did it all. If we believe and ask God to help us to obey and repent of our sins, He accepts us, because Jesus led a sinless life in our place."

Mila brushed her hand over a black, leather-bound book lying on the table. *That must be a Bible,* Mara thought, wondering why Mila hadn't opened it. *Father had a Bible like that,* she recalled, *but we thought it was so sacred that we were afraid to pick it up to read. Just having it in the house made us feel God was near.*

"So, that's how we're saved, Mara—by grace, through faith, as the Bible says." Mila started winding down. "God promises to change our hearts and minds if we trust Him and choose to obey. He transforms our characters so we want to do His good works. At the same time, those whom the devil deceives become like him in character, and they naturally do his evil works." Mila paused. "In the end, Mara, God will make all things right. The wicked will get their punishment and the righteous will get their reward. The great controversy will end, and the devil and sin will be no more, and there will be no more suffering or war.

"Well, Mara," she took a deep breath. She had been talking a long time and had run out of air. "That's enough for today, I think. We can study more from the Bible when you come back. Then I'll answer your questions about the Sabbath."

"Thank you so much, Mila. I never heard anyone explain it that way," Mara said, standing up to leave. "I'll come back on Saturday for more."

Walking the mile back home, Mara marveled. Though the questions she had come to ask hadn't been answered, a peace filled her heart. In a simple and understandable way, Mila had begun to open a door to heavenly treasures, and as Mara gazed in, she was entranced. She thought about what Mila had said and the kind of God her words had revealed. Ideas tumbled about in Mara's head: *God created men free to choose. And He warned Adam and Eve about the consequences of sin. He warns everyone. But He never forces us. Instead, He made every sacrifice, every provision, to save us. Those who died in the Flood could have been spared if they chose. Like the ark, heaven is open to all.*

Eagerly, she looked forward to her next visit the following week.

5
A Day Reserved for God

When Mara arrived at Mila's house the next Saturday afternoon, Mila's eight-year-old daughter, Dana, joined them at the table. The black, leather-bound Book lay open in front of her.

"Today we'll see what the Bible says about the Sabbath," Mila said. She turned to her daughter. "Dana, read for me the first three verses of Genesis chapter two."

Dana picked up the black Book and turned the pages to the beginning. Mara noticed how easily she seemed to find the passage. The little girl read aloud: "Thus the heavens and the earth were finished, and all the host of them. And on the seventh day God ended His work which he had made; and he rested on the seventh day from all his work which He had made. And God blessed the seventh day, and sanctified it; because that in it he had rested from all his work which God created and made."

"You see, Mara, the Bible says God made the world in six days and rested on the seventh day. He began on the first day of the week. Look at the calendar." She pointed to a small, faded calendar hanging on the wall near the wood-burning stove.

"It shows Sunday is the first day," Mara observed, her voice subdued. "The seventh day is Saturday."

"That's right, Mara. God rested on Saturday. The word *Sabbath* actually means 'rest.' When God rested, He blessed and made that day holy and special. That's what the Scripture says. Nowhere did God bless Sunday. It's just not in the Bible anywhere."

"But Saturday is a Jewish holy day, isn't it?" Mara countered, confusion clouding her face.

"There were no Jews in the Garden of Eden. Abraham, the father of the Jews, wasn't born until twenty-five hundred years later. God gave the Sabbath to Adam and Eve to be the day of worship for the human race, just like He gave marriage to the whole human race. Both the Sabbath and marriage originated in Eden. Both are for everybody. If the Sabbath is Jewish, then marriage must be Jewish too."

At that, Mara's eyebrows went up. She repositioned herself in her chair.

"The Jews kept the Sabbath because at that time they were the only people who worshiped the true God. Find the Ten Commandments," Mila directed her daughter. "They're in Exodus chapter twenty. Read the fourth commandment."

Dana found the text and read out loud: " 'Remember the sabbath day, to keep it holy. Six days shalt thou labour, and do all thy work: But the seventh day is the sabbath of the Lord thy God: in it thou shalt not do any work, thou, nor thy son, nor thy daughter, thy manservant, nor thy maidservant, nor thy cattle, nor thy stranger that is within thy gates: For in six days the Lord made heaven and earth, the sea, and all that in them is, and rested the seventh day: wherefore the Lord blessed the sabbath day, and hallowed it.' "

"God told us to remember because He knew people would forget. What makes God different from the false gods, Mara, is that He is the Creator God. Saturday reminds us of that fact. That is why we worship Him. Saturday is the only Sabbath in both the Old and New Testaments. Jesus kept the Sabbath when He lived on this earth. It says so in Luke four, sixteen." She turned to Dana. Dana opened the Bible to the New Testament and read: " 'And he came to Nazareth, where he had been brought up: and, as his custom was, he went into the synagogue on the sabbath day, and stood up for to read.' "

"Jesus even kept the Sabbath in the grave after He died. Dana, please find Luke twenty-three, verses fifty-four through fifty-six." Once again the little girl quickly found the text and read it: " 'That day was the preparation, and the sabbath drew on. And the women also, which came with him from Galilee, followed after, and beheld the sepulcher, and how his body was laid. And they returned, and prepared spices and ointments; and rested the sabbath day according to the commandment.' "

"Did you hear that, Mara?" Mila asked. "The women rested according to the commandment, and Jesus rested in the grave. So His resurrection on Sunday only confirmed the Sabbath. It didn't change it. He simply arose on the first work day of the week. Read Acts seventeen, two, Dana."

" 'And Paul, as his manner was, went in unto them, and three sabbath days reasoned with them out of the scriptures.' "

"This is important, Mara. Paul became a Christian many years after Jesus' resurrection. Yet He worshiped on Saturday. God appeared to him, but He never told him the Sabbath was changed. Paul was sent to the Gentiles. That shows the Sabbath is for Gentiles, too." Mila paused. "Not only that, Jesus expected His followers to be keeping the same seventh-day Sabbath even after Paul's death—many years later when Jerusalem was destroyed. He talked about that in Matthew twenty-four, verses nineteen and twenty." Dana turned to the verses and read: " 'And woe unto them that are with child, and to them that give suck in those days! But pray ye that your flight be not in the winter, neither on the sabbath day.' "

"Wouldn't God tell us somewhere if there had been a change? There just isn't any record of that. And why would God change His special day to a pagan one? It makes no sense." Mila paused. "Jesus specifically said that He did not do that." She quoted from memory Matthew 5:17, 18. " 'Think not that I am come to destroy the law, or the prophets; I am not come to destroy, but to fulfil. For verily I say unto you, Till heaven and earth pass, one jot or one tittle shall in no wise pass from the law, till all be fulfilled.' Those are the words of Jesus. God's law is eternal."

All the while Mila spoke and Dana read, Mara sat absorbing their words. Now she said, "But, Mila, if Jesus didn't change the Sabbath, how did it get changed?"

"Human beings changed God's law in violation of His Word," Mila replied. "But God declares that He will do away with every tradition contrary to His law." She turned to her daughter. "Dana, read Matthew fifteen, verses three, nine, and thirteen. When Dana found the texts, she read: " 'But he answered and said unto them, Why do ye also transgress the commandment of God by your tradition? . . . But in vain they do worship me, teaching for doctrines the commandments of men. . . . Every plant, which my heavenly Father hath not planted, shall be rooted up.' "

"In fact," Mila continued, "God forbids anyone to add or take away from His Word." She mentioned Deuteronomy 4:2 and Revelation 22:18, 19 but she didn't ask Dana to read them.

Mila allowed Mara time to absorb all that she had heard. It was a lot for her to take in at once. She refilled their water glasses from a jug on the counter. As they both sipped, Mara pondered what she was learning. "It's like a birthday." The words fell out. "Sabbath is like the birthday of the world."

"Sure enough!" Mila replied, surprised and pleased by Mara's insightful observation. "Nobody can change your birthday, can they?"

"Read those last verses again, Mila," Mara asked after they had discussed the subject a while. By then, Dana had gone off to play.

Mila's face flushed, and she lowered her eyes. "I can't read, Mara," she said, her voice just above a whisper. "That's why my Dana reads for me. I didn't tell you last week because I was afraid you might not come back."

"But . . . but you know so much! You talk like a preacher. How did you learn all these things?" Mara asked, stunned by Mila's confession. Here was a woman who knew the Bible better than anyone she had ever come in contact with, yet Mila was illiterate.

"Oh, I've been memorizing verses for years. I listen to the preacher, try to connect a few words with the texts so I can ask Dana to find them for me afterward." Mila paused before adding softly, "God blesses my mind." Then she confided happily, "Last year Dana started school. Now she's teaching me to read, but I'm not ready yet."

"Where can I buy a Bible?" Mara asked. "I want to read God's Word for myself."

"I'll order one from Šabac. You can probably have it by next week," Mila promised.

Mara's face suddenly clouded as she spoke softly. "You know, Mila, I do believe Saturday is God's Sabbath. Johann was right. But how can I rest from sunset Friday to sunset Saturday every week while the family works? What would they think? How could I explain?"

"Don't give up now, Mara. I can see that God is guiding you. Pray and believe. I'll pray for you, too," Mila replied. "If God is calling you to obey, He will make it possible. Remember, God can do all things if we believe."

And so began Mara's Bible studies, with Mila telling Dana the verses to look up and then Dana reading them aloud. Mila and Mara discussed these texts earnestly. Walking home again afterward, Mara prayed. She was learning a new way, using words from her heart instead of from a prayer book.

Dear God, she prayed silently, *You know all things. You know my heart. These sessions with Mila have ignited a fire in my soul that won't be quenched. I thirst to know more. My visits to the Orthodox church lifted my spirits in reverent worship, but they left me as ignorant of the Scriptures when I left as when I came in. I couldn't understand the priest's words in the Old Slavic language. In these two visits with Mila, I have learned more about the Bible than I ever expected. If You want me to keep Your Sabbath, please make it possible. Thank You, Jesus. Amen.*

When Mara arrived for their third study session, Mila handed her a package, saying, "Here's your Bible."

"My own Bible!" Mara exclaimed, holding the Book reverently to her heart, her eyes sparkling.

She took the Bible home and read it hungrily, stealing a few minutes out of each day—early in the morning before the others arose or at night while the family slept. As she continued her weekly studies with Mila, she felt God very close to her. Thus immersed in Scripture, her understanding and love for God steadily grew. She had come to know Him personally, as her best Friend, loving Savior, and Lord of her life. Her faith struck deep roots. Taking the Sabbath problem to God, she fasted and prayed for wisdom, a practice she continued the rest of her life.

The answer came a few days later after talking with her sister-in-law Lila and explaining her problem. "I don't see why that can't be arranged," Lila said. "I can take your place on Saturdays, if you relieve me on one of my assigned days. I'm sure someone will be willing to look after the twins in your absence."

"Oh, Lila, how can I ever thank you!" Mara gushed, giving her a hug. When she consulted the other women, they, too, seemed satisfied with the adjustment. Alone afterward, Mara lifted a prayer of gratitude and praise to God. Whenever she filled in for Lila, she did more work than required, wanting to lighten Lila's load for the following day.

Lord, help me maintain good relationships within the family. I must not let my desire to serve You keep me from fulfilling my responsibilities at home, she often prayed.

And so early the next Sabbath, for the first time, Mara met with two small groups from neighboring villages who gathered to study and worship in the modest home of the Borovich family in Uzveće. Neighbors and friends gaped as they saw her, clad in her best dress and hat, walking past them toward Uzveće—in the opposite direction of Glušci's Orthodox church to which she had formerly walked every Sunday. After the meeting, she rushed home to nurse her boys and then return to Mila's house in the afternoon for another study.

"What is this thing you're doing on Saturday?" Ilija asked Mara one Sabbath.

As best she could, Mara explained.

"It's not really a foreign idea to me," he said. "When I was a prisoner of war in Budapest, the Jewish brewer in charge of me would shut down his brewery from sunset Friday to sunset Saturday every week. But he was a Jew. You're not. Frankly, Mara, I don't understand. But go ahead, if it makes you happy. I don't expect it will change anything."

How wrong he was Ilija would soon discover. Everything about their lives hung in the balance.

6
An Urgent Message

"Today we'll study about Jesus' second coming," Mila said the next Sabbath afternoon when Mara arrived to continue her studies. Dana was not there.

"You know, Mara, Jesus promised to return to earth," Mila began. "He told His disciples so. Can you find John fourteen, verses one through three? It's near the beginning of the New Testament."

Now that she had her own Bible and was becoming familiar with its contents, Mara wanted to find the texts herself. She turned the pages to the bookmark set between Old and New Testaments, then leafed through the Gospels to the book of John, and read: " 'Let not your heart be troubled: ye believe in God, believe also in me. In my Father's house are many mansions: if it were not so, I would have told you. I go to prepare a place for you. And if I go and prepare a place for you, I will come again, and receive you unto myself; that where I am, there ye may be also.' "

"Think of it, Mara. The King of the universe wants us to spend eternity with Him!" Mila's face glowed as she talked. "Jesus even told us how He would come so no one would be deceived. Read Matthew chapter twenty-four, verses twenty-seven, thirty, and thirty-one," Mila instructed. "Matthew is the first book in the New Testament."

Mara read, " 'For as the lightning cometh out of the east, and shineth even unto the west; so shall also the coming of the Son of man be . . . and they shall see the Son of man coming in the clouds of heaven with power and great glory. And he shall send his angels with a great sound of a trumpet, and they shall gather together his elect from the four winds, from one end of heaven to the other.' "

"And Revelation one, seven. Read it, Mara. Revelation is the last book in the Bible."

Mara turned to the back and read, " 'Behold, he cometh with clouds; and every eye shall see him, and they also which pierced him: and all kindreds of the earth shall wail because of him. Even so, Amen.' "

"This is a bright and glorious happening, a loud and noisy event. No one can miss it. It won't happen in secret. Jesus came the first time to save the world. He comes the second time to judge the world and give the righteous their reward," Mila added. "It says so in Matthew sixteen, twenty-seven."

Mara turned back to the bookmark and looked for the chapter. When she found it, she read, " 'For the Son of man shall come in the glory of His Father with his angels; and then he shall reward every man according to his works.' "

"Tell me, Mila, when will this happen?" Mara asked, eagerly.

"Nobody knows the exact day or hour, but Jesus said to watch and be ready. Turn to Revelation again. Chapter twenty, verses eleven, twelve, and fifteen."

Mara did so. She began reading. " 'And I saw a great white throne, and him that sat on it, from whose face the earth and the heaven fled away; and there was found no place for them. And I saw the dead, small and great, stand before God; and the books were opened; and another book was opened, which is the book of life: and the dead were judged out of those things which were written in the books. . . . And whosoever was not found written in the book of life was cast into the lake of fire.' "

"That fire is reserved for the devil and his evil angels, but all those who follow him will burn with him," Mila added. When Mila looked at Mara again, the blood had drained from her face. "What is it Mara? Are you all right?"

"Oh, Mila, how terrible that will be, the lake of fire! What must I do to have my name written in the book of life?"

"When we repent and choose to follow Jesus, our name goes in the book of life. If we repent and confess our sins, God promises to forgive us and cleanse us from all unrighteousness. Then we're ready to be baptized. For baptism, we have to be old enough to make these decisions. Remember John the Baptist? He baptized people in the Jordan River by immersion. In baptism symbolically we die to sin, our old life is buried, and we are resurrected to a new life."

"That's beautiful, Mila. I'm ready. When can I be baptized?" Mara asked eagerly.

"Well, you need to keep studying so that you understand what you're promising. Anyway, you can't get baptized now. It's the dead of winter; the weather is too cold. We have no indoor baptistries, and the rivers are frozen. By spring you'll be ready. It will be warm then."

"Oh, no, Mila, I can't wait that long," Mara replied, wilting. "Jesus might come, and I want to be ready."

"There's really no hurry, Mara. God knows your heart. It's not likely that He'll come that soon."

"But how can you be so sure? What if He does? I need to be baptized right away," Mara insisted.

"All right, Mara," Mila finally agreed. "I'll send a message to the pastor in Šabac and see what he says."

A few days later, the reply came. A brave and dedicated first elder had consented to perform the baptism. It was in his home that the group in the district town of Šabac met. Mara was thrilled.

Early on the designated Sabbath, January 18, 1930, Mara, together with Mila and three other local members from Uzveće, rode the twelve miles to Šabac in an open, horse-drawn carriage. Two men from the Šabac group met them there. "We had to chop through a foot of ice," one of them told the group. "You're a brave lady. We'll take you to the place. There's just enough space for you to be baptized."

And so on that sunny, windless day on the shore of the Sava River, ten stalwart souls formed a circle of prayer. The words of the song "Just As I Am" floated over the ice as two white-robed figures broke away from the group and stepped into the freezing water just far enough for Mara to be immersed.

The elder lifted his hand over Mara's head and prayed, then quickly dipped her backward into the water. They emerged cold and shivering, their robes clinging to their bodies and their teeth chattering. Waiting arms quickly wrapped them in warm woolen blankets, gave them towels with which to dry themselves, and held up other blankets so each could change into dry clothing because there were no shelters or homes near-by. Dry and dressed and wrapped in still other blankets, the two brave souls and eight other happy members rode to the first elder's home to celebrate with a hot meal.

Baptized now, and a *bona fide* church member, Mara felt warmed by the smile of God. Everything around her now seemed somehow more glorious and new. She was ready to meet Jesus.

Unknown to her, however, storm clouds were beginning to gather on the horizon. A crisis loomed just ahead. Would she be ready to meet it?

7
Storm Clouds Gather

"Ilija, I got baptized," Mara told her husband one evening shortly afterward, as they prepared for bed. Her heart overflowed with a joy she could not keep back.

"Baptized? What do you mean? You were baptized in the Holy Orthodox Church when you were a baby." He looked bewildered.

"I know, but that was my parents' choice, not mine. I was baptized now as an adult, like John the Baptist baptized, in a river."

"A river?" His brows lowered. "Where? Everything is frozen."

"In the Sava. Some members cut through the ice. The first elder from Šabac baptized me." She smiled, seeing his concern. "Not to worry, Ilija. Everything is fine. I didn't get sick. This baptism means I promise to follow Jesus."

"I thought that is what you have been doing, Mara. You've always gone to church."

"Yes, but now I understand so much better what that means—what the Bible says. It makes me very happy. I wish you could join me."

Ilija sighed. "I can see that, Mara, and I'm glad for you. But these new ideas of yours baffle me. I'm a Serb. Why should I go to an American church? I have my own." He threw out his hands. "So . . . does your baptism make you an American now? Or a Jew? I don't know what you are anymore."

"No, Ilija. I'm still Serbian. I still believe in the same God as before. Except that now I know Him so much better. I follow the Bible teachings more closely. I'm a Seventh-day Adventist. That's the name of my church."

"Like I said, Mara, your new religion baffles me."

Word of Mara's baptism soon spread through the village, and neighbors began to inquire. "Ilija, I heard Mara got baptized into another church. Does she have a new name now?" Krsta, a neighbor, asked Ilija one day at the mill.

Ilija shrugged. "Why don't you ask Mara?" he replied. "She's over there." He pointed.

Mara stood at the flour bin where the family stored the portion of flour they kept as their grinding fee. Spotting her there, Krsta approached.

"*Tetka* [a respectful form of address] Mara, I heard you got baptized." He fiddled with his fingers. "Do you have a new name now? What should I call you?"

Mara chuckled. "No, Krsta, I don't have a new name. I was baptized like Jesus was. Remember? John the Baptist baptized Him in the Jordan River when He was a grown man. I didn't get another name."

"Well, *Tetka* Mara, I don't understand these things, you know. I don't read holy books like you do. So then I can still call you Mara?" His brows went up.

"Yes, Krsta. I'm still Mara." She smiled.

Winter snows soon began to melt. Purple and yellow crocuses peeked out, and buds began to sprout on tree branches as spring arrived and nature breathed new life. Warm Sabbath afternoons found Mara sitting on a chair beneath the charred old apple tree that had survived the war and under which Jovan had buried their gold ducats before fleeing. It stood beside their new house and continued to live and grow. The scene was always the same, though on cooler days she wrapped herself in a sweater or blanket—Bible in her lap, her spectacles on her nose, a double-folded blanket cushioning the wooden chair on which she sat, and a small stool on which she rested her feet. Her twins often slept in their cradle by her side or played in the grass at her feet, while Mara told Bible stories to Nata and Vera.

As hired workers, carrying on their duties, passed by, they greeted Mara respectfully, removing their hats and nodding. She heard their whispers as they nudged each other. "Mara is reading God's Word!" Among these people of the Eastern tradition there was a simple faith, an inherent fear of God, and a reverence for His Word.

May arrived, and though this year's wheat fields were still green and harvest more than a month away, there were always horse- or ox-drawn carts waiting with their owners for their grain to be processed into flour.

One day Mara asked Ilija for permission to attend a large church meeting in Novi Sad, a city some distance away. "Church members are coming from all parts of Yugoslavia," she explained. "Local members will put us up in their houses overnight."

Ilija hesitated. "It's not customary for a woman to leave her family and go off on her own like that to another city for a weekend, Mara," he said. "You know that."

"I do, Ilija, but this is a church group, and I'll be going with Mila and three other women. Milorad said he'd drive me to the bus station. And I already asked Milorad's daughter-in-law Vukosava if she would help nurse the boys in my absence. Her baby is only a month younger, and she's helped me on occasion when I ran out of milk. It takes a lot to satisfy two growing boys." Mara's enthusiasm captured Ilija, and he reluctantly agreed.

The church meeting took place at the end of June, and neighbors noted Mara's absence. Soon word got out in the village that Mara had gone to a "conference." The men began to wonder. While waiting for their grain to be processed, they frequently passed the time talking. This time, the subject was Mara.

"Say, Ilija, how could you let your wife take off on her own like that?" a customer inquired. "Who ever heard of women going to a conference?"

"Well, Živko, times are changing. Maybe we need to change with them," Ilija replied, hoisting a bag of flour onto a waiting ox cart.

"Independent women—definitely trouble, if you ask me," another chided, shaking his head. "Who's the boss in your house anyway?"

"Must be my Mara," Ilija replied good-naturedly, and went about his business.

"I hear Mara's become a Jew," someone else remarked.

"No, Duško, she goes to a Christian church on Saturday, not a synagogue. She says it's according to the Bible."

The townspeople simply did not understand. Some, especially the men, seemed to take Mara's independent actions as a personal affront, even a threat. Of the nations in Europe, Serbs were among the few with no history of ever persecuting Jews, and many Serbs had lost their lives in the Great War trying to protect them. So it wasn't prejudice. Ilija let most of the men's remarks roll off his back.

One day Ilija made a trip to another town to purchase an ash tree, which would be cut into lumber at the family's sawmill.

"So you're from Glušci," the owner of the tree, a woman, remarked as she wrote up the sale. "Do you happen to know the owner of the grain mill there? From what I hear, he's able to manage his business, but not his wife!" she laughed.

Surprised and embarrassed, Ilija felt his face turn scarlet. "As a matter of fact, I'm that man," he acknowledged.

Now, it was the woman's turn to blush. Avoiding his eyes, she began to spout profuse apologies and quickly concluded the sale. Ilija could not leave the place soon enough. Riding home in the carriage afterward, still burning with humiliation, he recalled the times his peers had laughed at his expense. The gibes heaped dishonor on his good name and reputation of which he was proud. Now his wife's infamy had spread to other towns. "This is the last straw," he promised himself, his jaw tightening.

8
Mara's Test of Faith

That evening a relentless rain beat down on the tile roof of their house while the children slept, oblivious to the drama playing out in another room. By now, the twins were almost a year old; Vera was three, and Nata was ten. Leka, eighteen years old, still lived with her grandparents, though she often came for prolonged visits.

In their room, Mara sat on the bed, watching Ilija pace. He carried himself with such dignity that for a moment her mind flashed back to the day she had first laid eyes on him in his Austrian tunic at the fair in her former village. She had fallen in love with him then, and she loved him still. *There's nothing I wouldn't do to please him,* she thought.

But now as he related the events of the day, his thick brows hovered low over his eyes, and his face took on a grim expression. Pacing back and forth, he came to Mara and stopped. Looking off to her side, he issued his ultimatum.

"I've been very patient, Mara, but this has gone too far. You don't know what it's been like for me—my peers mocking me. I've become a laughingstock. I can't take it anymore." Mara searched his eyes; they were still the deep, dark eyes that had captivated her the first time she had looked into them. But there was something else in them now. She thought she saw pain.

"You have to forget this religion of yours, Mara, and be like the other women." He sighed. "Or . . . or . . . I'll have to ask you to leave." As this last sentence fell out of his mouth, he sat down heavily in a chair, holding his head in his hands.

Mara drew back horrified, his words exploding in her mind. In that instant, her happy world shattered, dissolving into rubble at her feet. She could feel the panic swelling inside. For a long while she could not reply.

"Leave, Ilija? You want me to go?" she said, finding her voice. She stared in disbelief at her husband. "But where should I go? How would I manage? What would become of my girls? Who would care for my babies?" She said the words calmly, though her mind screamed inside.

"The children will be fine with me. The other women can help care for them, and Nata is old enough now to help."

Mara sat stunned and shaken, sifting among the ruins. Her mind raced frantically, desperately. Questions pounded inside her head. *How could Ilija ask me to go? What has happened to the love of my life? No, he doesn't really want me to go, I can see that. It's just that he's a man, and men are proud. No doubt he thought I'd give in when presented with his ultimatum. That everything would be as it was before.* She heaved a sigh. *He's wrong, so wrong.* From somewhere within she finally summoned the strength to continue.

"Ilija, you know I would do anything for you. You and the children are my life." She sat forward, reached out to him, then dropped her hand and talked to the wooden floor. "But I can't do what you ask, Ilija. I can't do it." Her hands were clenched so tightly that the knuckles turned white. She shut her eyes.

"When I was baptized, I promised to obey God always. He comes first. I couldn't live with myself if I didn't follow my conscience." Her voice broke, then strengthened as she lifted her eyes to his and went on. "I'll leave, Ilija, if you want me to." She said the words but clung to hope.

Ilija's face sagged, and he turned to the wall, the color drawn from his face. Her words, too, hit hard, and as he stared blankly, his shoulders slumped.

Outside, the rain pounded. Huge drops clattered on the roof and ran from the eaves in torrents, like tears from the eyes of God shed in sympathy for her plight. A melancholy wind wailed and sighed dismally.

"I need time to find a place." The words came out in a whisper.

Ilija got up and walked to the window, looking outside. Without turning, he nodded agreement, then strode to the door. He opened it and walked into the corridor. The click of the door behind him echoed in the solitude that surrounded Mara. She heard the outside door close. Sitting alone on the bed, Ilija's stinging words still rang in her ears and reverberated in the empty room—*"I'll have to ask you to leave! Leave! Leave! Leave!"*

Over the pounding rain tumbled a great roll of thunder. The wind outside grew stronger, battering the house. Suddenly Mara began to shake. Collapsing into bed fully clothed, she kicked off her shoes and pulled the sheet over her. *Oh, Lord. Oh, God. What am I to do?* For a long time she pleaded with God until finally falling asleep.

In the morning, Mara awoke before sunrise, her eyes puffy. The place beside her in the bed remained untouched. Ilija must have slept in the mill as he often did when the mill ran round the clock. A glance out the window told her the rain had stopped. The clouds of the night had thinned out and scattered in small clumps. The morning looked dull, gray, and depressing—like her spirits. Leaving the twins in Petra's care, she put on her sweater and stepped outside. Her heart felt like lead in her chest as she directed her weary feet toward Mila's house. It was Mila who had led her to read and understand Bible truths. Perhaps now she could help her figure out what to do. She made her way in a squall of emotions, skirting the puddles in the road from the rain of the night before. Frogs bellowed from water-filled ditches on either side. Today the road to Mila's house seemed much too long.

Sitting with Mila at the old table where on happier days they had studied and her heart had been filled with joy, Mara spilled out her story. At this same familiar table the stories of Christ's love and compassion had first thrilled her heart. Here she had come to know a God who longed to be her Friend and Savior. Now everything seemed changed and dark. "Does God expect such a sacrifice from me? Could this be His will for my life? Must I give up my family in order to please Him?" she slung her questions at Mila as her friend tried to comfort her.

"I don't know, Mara. We Serbs believe in being purified by our suffering. I believe God will work this out for you. It's hard." Mila paused. "I know an influential woman in Šabac who could get you work as a housekeeper. Adventists are known as honest workers. I'll try to get word to her. Until you find something, Mara, you can stay with me."

When Mara returned home, she found Ilija waiting stone-faced and haggard-looking. Without displaying emotion, Mara told him she would be ready to leave the house the next day. He winced at the words.

That night, and far into the morning hours, Mara lay alone in her bed, pleading with God. *Lord, have You forsaken me? How can I leave my children? My boys are so young. You gave them to me. Will you now take them away? You promised in Your Word to answer prayers. Please help me now. Take care of my precious children.*

The deep, dense darkness that hung over her began to lift, and a calm infused her soul with peace. In her solitude she sensed an unseen Presence. God was with her in this storm. She groaned in exhaustion and fell asleep.

Early the next morning, the sun's rays peeked through the window on Mara's sleeping form. When she awoke and tried to get out of bed, she discovered she could not move. She called out to Nata.

The doctor who came was unable to diagnose the cause of her paralysis. "Ilija, Mara needs total rest. You must not move her. Her condition could easily worsen," he cautioned. "In her present state, she might even die."

Ilija knew Mara was not faking. "This is God's way of telling me He wants you to stay here, isn't it?" he conceded some time after the doctor left. Mara did not answer, but her heart leaped with new hope.

A week later the doctor returned to find Mara out of bed and walking around as if nothing had happened. She had recovered completely from the paralysis without medication and with no ill effects. "This is indeed a miracle!" the doctor exclaimed.

Although Ilija did not ask Mara to leave home again, the snide remarks of his peers did not cease. Ilija tried to ignore them, but the situation continued to take its toll.

9
The Crisis Continues

Thirteen miles away, Mara's two brothers lived in a village with their families and father in their own *zadruga*. Hoping they could give him some advice, Ilija decided to visit the brothers.

When Ilija related the situation, Petar, Mara's younger brother, shrugged it off. "So she goes to another church! What does it matter? Most of us don't go to church at all, though we consider ourselves Orthodox Christians."

However, Mladen, Mara's older brother, took her actions much more seriously. "She's dishonored the family, that's what she's done." His eyes flared with anger. "Whatever has gotten into my sister, I can tell you this. If she were my wife or one of my daughters—all six still live at home, you know—she would not be welcome in my house." His voice sounded confident. "As far as I'm concerned, Ilija, you have my permission to do whatever you want with my sister. If I don't accept her into my house, she'll have nowhere to go. Sooner or later, she'll come to her senses." So Mladen convinced Ilija to fall in with his plans. He promised to visit Ilija in the near future—on Ilija's *Slava*. His family's saint was Ignatius, and his day fell on January 2.

One afternoon Milorad, came by Mara's house. He had been out of town trading grain for clothing, sugar, fuel oil, and a few other staples for the family. He loved Mara's twins as his own. When he came in, Cveja was crying and Mara was rocking him in her lap.

"What's wrong, Mara? He looks so thin and wrinkled. Which one is it?"

"It's Cveja. He can't hold food or liquids. Everything comes out." Her voice was heavy with concern. "Voja had diarrhea too, but the medicine the doctor prescribed helped him. We've tried everything, Milorad. But Cveja is getting worse. I'm afraid he might not survive!"

"Oh, Mara! There must be something. I heard of a doctor who uses old-fashioned natural remedies. I can take you to him right now if you want. It can't hurt to try."

And so, leaving Voja with Ilija, Mara bundled Cveja in her arms and climbed into the carriage with Milorad to ride eight miles to the doctor, who lived in another town.

The elderly doctor was preparing to close his office when they arrived, but after taking one look at Cveja, he decided to see him. "My daughter," he said after the examination, "all I can offer you is a simple folk remedy. Only God can help your son." He told her to cook barley and give Cveja a glassful of the barley water four to five times a day.

Upon reaching home, Mara did as the doctor ordered, though the simplicity of the prescribed remedy did not impress her. "Oh, Lord, please let this help. You are the Great Physician," she prayed before offering Cveja half a glass of the cooled barley water. He drank it slowly—and it stayed down. A short while later, Mara gave him another dose. That night, for the first time in weeks, Cveja slept through the night. "It's a miracle! Thank You, Lord," Mara exclaimed.

The next day Mara repeated the doses throughout the day, increasing the amount of barley water and adding a slice of toast. Cveja drank and ate it all. Within a few days he recovered and began eating normally. Mara could not stop praising God for saving her son. Ten days later, Cveja had gained almost a pound, and his skin and face looked fresher and fuller.

Before the twins' first birthday, they were already babbling, even before they walked. In the evenings, while sitting in their crib, they talked incessantly to each other. Voja walked first. Cveja, still weak from his bout of diarrhea, tried to pull himself up by holding on to his brother's clothing. After several attempts that ended in their both falling to the floor, howling as they lay flat on their backs, Cveja took his first step.

The local cabinetmaker had made a baby carriage of wood, including the wheels. It looked more like a mobile crib with a steering bar. Nata proudly pulled her brothers around the farm with Vera tagging behind. At the grain mill, customers and workers alike crowded around, trying to tell the twins apart while Ilija beamed with pride.

Once the twins started walking, there was no stopping them. Vera followed them everywhere like a shadow in a skirt, singing, "My sweet brothers, my sweet brothers." Dressed identically in outfits Mara had sewn on her Singer sewing machine purchased in Šabac, the twins confounded observers. Even Ilija found it difficult to tell them apart. "Cveja's face is thinner. See, his hairline comes to a V on his forehead," Mara would point out.

Though the boys had the run of the place, Nata always lingered nearby. She baby-sat them after school while their mother worked. When she completed the four mandatory years of grade school, she did not continue her schooling. The eight-year high school was in the district town of Šabac, and she would have to leave home to attend. In the agrarian economy of that time and place, higher education was not considered essential—especially not for girls.

Before long, the bright colors of fall began to fade into the dull drab of winter, and chill winds blew in. Though planting and harvesting ceased, animals still needed to be fed and let out to pasture, and cows needed to be milked. Customers brought their dried corn and grain to the grain mill for processing all year round.

On cold winter evenings, the extended family gathered in the communal kitchen to eat and to socialize, warmed by the crackling fire in the open brick oven. The glow of kerosene table lamps cast weird shadows on the white walls, while adults talked and laughed and children played and romped about. Mihajlo often plucked the single-stringed *gusle,* chanting the ancient ballads of Serbia to its monotonous sound, recalling the heroes of old, which were household names.

The second day of January dawned cold and bleak. A heavy snow had fallen the day before and left a thick white blanket over the land. It was Saint Ignatius's Day. Friends and family braved the weather to make the trip to Ilija's house. Mara's brother, Mladen, with his long black mustache and flowing sheep-skin cape, arrived with Petar and their wives in a horse-drawn sleigh. One of Mihajlo's sons brought *Prota* Mihajlo in the family's beautifully carved sleigh. "Peace be to this house," the priest said, crossing himself as he entered.

Mara had not seen the priest since the day she presented him with the tapestry for the church, yet his greeting was as gracious now as when she had attended his church regularly. He had baptized the boys as infants and was happy to see them now.

Sixty guests arranged themselves on benches on both sides of two long rows of tables in the dining hall of the new house. On this formal occasion, the priest sat in the place of honor at the head table. Family members followed by seniority.

A variety of traditional dishes covered the tables. Because this *Slava* fell during the six-week Advent fast that preceded the Eastern Orthodox Christmas, fish, cheese, and vegetarian dishes took the place of the usually plentiful meats. Rivers were frozen, and fish were unavailable locally, so two days earlier, Milorad's oldest son had traveled to the Adriatic coast. He had returned the night before with a load of fish packed in coarse salt.

From a seat diagonally across the table from Ilija, Mladen shot him a glance. Ilija turned to the priest. "*Prota* Mihajlo, I have a problem," he said quietly. "Mara has changed her religion." He glanced at Mladen who nodded him on. "*Prota* Mihajlo, I ask your permission to divorce my wife."

Ilija's words fell like sand on a fire, smothering the joviality of the occasion for Mara and making her shudder. She had thought the crisis ended. Now here she was, helpless and vulnerable again. Everyone knew she attended a different church, and among those present sat several of the men who had thoughtlessly taunted Ilija. She felt every eye boring into her, and she dropped her gaze to the floor, wishing it would open up and swallow her.

As the priest of the village, *Prota* Mihajlo had certainly noticed Mara's absences at liturgy for more than a year. Looking thoughtfully at Ilija, he sat forward, tapping his finger on the table, and replied.

"Ilija, the church does not grant divorce without cause. Even though Mara goes to a different church, she's still a Christian. She believes in the same God and in the Holy Trinity. And I know she hasn't committed adultery. Ilija, you have no grounds for a divorce."

Then pointing his finger at Ilija, he continued. "I'm going to tell you something that may surprise you." In the subdued room, curious ears strained to listen. There were not many secrets in a little village. "People say that many chains lead to heaven, but only one is a golden chain that leads to God's throne." He paused reflectively. "Who knows! Maybe Mara has found that golden chain. Maybe the rest of us are all wrong!"

Ilija drew back. He glanced at Mladen, whose face reflected his own dismay. Milorad, who had been listening intently, stood up and spoke with the authority of the head of the clan. "*Prota* Mihajlo has spoken. There is no reason to criticize Mara—or Ilija." He looked at each one in the room. "We are democratic, reasonable people. Each person has a right to choose. Others live peacefully in our midst. Why shouldn't one of our own?" He looked at Ilija. "We will allow Mara to serve God in her own way and pray for us."

Relief and gratitude washed over Mara's face, and she sat in awe of what had just taken place. Lifting her eyes, she met the warm gaze of the priest. Again she had been brought to the brink, this time saved by a most unlikely angel wearing a black robe and sporting a flowing gray beard.

If the priest's declaration had settled the matter for Ilija and the men in his family, it was not so for Mladen. As guests took their leave, he pulled Ilija aside. "Don't give up yet, Ilija," he urged. "I'll find another opportunity to straighten my sister out. She'll give in. You'll see."

10
Mara's Midnight Errand

By now Mara had read her Bible completely through and was starting to read it again. Ever since the priest's proclamation, she had found
acceptance with family and friends, and her confidence grew. Customers at the grain mill no longer taunted Ilija. Under the influence of the
priest, their attitudes changed. Peace returned once more to Mara's bat-
tered spirit.

Spring rains came and went. The sweltering heat of summer passed.
Winter wheat had been harvested in July and lay drying in the granary.
Plums, harvested in August, were fermenting in vats preparatory to
making plum brandy for export. Soon grapes would be picked and
pressed for wine. The leaves of Mara's favorite apple tree, under which
she spent so many summer Sabbath hours, blazed bright orange-yellow,
its surviving branches now stretching thirty feet across like a canopy of
fire. *Like me, this tree has weathered many storms—and survived,* she often thought. In its shelter she found comfort.

Rows of acacia trees that bordered the fields burst into banners of
yellow gold. In recent days, large fields of clover had been cut, dried, and
stored for feed hay. Turned-over soil left broad black stretches across the
landscape into which winter wheat had been sown.

A bright white full moon lit the midnight sky one night and cast an
eerie glow over the fields, as a lone dark figure walked in the middle of
the road. Short and stocky, with a sack slung over her left shoulder and
a long walking stick in her right hand, she moved deliberately, taking

long strides. In the sleeping silence of the town, the soft footfalls of her sandal-shod feet and the tap of her walking stick on the compact-gravel road resonated its repetitive rhythm.

It was Mara. In her dark kerchief, dress, sweater, and woolen stockings, her figure merged with the warm, black September night. From time to time as she walked, she shifted the heavy sack to her other shoulder and continued her pilgrimage. No one at home but Nata knew of her mysterious errand.

Somewhere in the distance a cock crowed at the midnight moon. Then another echoed his nocturnal call. Mara was not afraid of walking alone in the dark. She could stroll calmly through a cemetery alone at midnight, where strong men, brave in battle, quaked. What she did fear was snakes, even the harmless variety she encountered occasionally in the garden. The story of the serpent in the Garden of Eden who beguiled Eve into sin intensified her dread.

The night air, tinged with the subtle scent of ripe corn tassels, smelled fresh and clean. Mara breathed it in deeply. She cherished these special quiet times alone in the darkness with her God. In her imagination, the two of them were the only ones in the whole world who were awake and busy about their business.

She liked to survey the starry sky, which scintillated above her like a diamond-studded velvet mantle, and wonder what mysteries lay deep within its secret recesses. What worlds, what life stirred unperceived, unknown, where the sovereign God reigned gloriously over all? These times of solitude lifted her spirit to another plane, imbuing her soul with a deeper love for the sacred.

Ahead, on her left, loomed a long stockade fence that enclosed a trio of houses now silhouetted in the moonlight. Here, three brothers—Krsta, Živadin, and Dušan—lived with their families. Their seven dogs of various sizes and mixed breeds were kept chained during the day and let loose at night to guard the compound. As she neared the first house where Živadin, the youngest of the brothers, lived, his dogs started barking. All along the fence, the other dogs joined in a chorus of bays and barks, howls and growls as she neared.

Suddenly, chains clattered and clanged. Mara froze in her steps. Helplessly, she watched as one by one all seven dogs, at different points, leaped nimbly over the fence and onto the road. Each dragged behind it a chain with a wooden stump tied to the end, intended to prevent the dog from doing what it had just done.

As the dogs charged noisily toward her, barking and clanging, Mara suddenly raised her stick and pointed it at them. They ran right up to her, quieted down, and lined up in a row, their ears pointed, their tails raised. She kept her stick directed at them as she continued walking. As soon as she passed them, the dogs began barking again, broke formation, and one by one leaped back over the fence into the yard. Chains and stumps clanged and bumped after them.

Early the next morning, farmers began to line up at the grain mill with their newly harvested and dried wheat, ready to be ground into flour. With the wheat harvest ended, the grinding season was in full swing. Heavily loaded horse-drawn wagons and ox carts arrived, depositing loads of four to thirty sacks of wheat.

Hundreds of sacks, weighing from one hundred to more than two hundred pounds each, rose in crisscross layers to the open-beamed ceiling of the mill's upper platform. Other sacks already converted to flour waited on the lower platform for pick up. Soon the corn harvest would begin, and the mill would continue working around the clock through December before slowing down. At any given time five to ten workers assisted Ilija, while ten to twenty people waited for their flour.

Around midmorning, an unshaven and tired-looking Živadin arrived at the mill and stopped in the doorway on the lower level. Ilija, looking distinguished in his black-on-black braid-bound vest, gray britches, and black felt hat, was rubbing some flour between his fingers to test its texture. The tag on the sack in front of him specified the flour be ground very fine.

When Živadin spotted Ilija, he started to call out, then, changed his mind and turned to leave. He stopped at the threshold of the platform, looked back, then seemed to settle himself to wait. Fidgeting nervously, his small eyes stared blankly at the wooden platform while his lips moved in silent rehearsal of his speech.

"Greetings, Živadin," Ilija called out cheerfully. He had noticed Živadin standing just outside the open doorway, deep in thought and empty-handed. "What brings you here, my friend?"

"Ilija," Živadin began timidly, "I came because something strange happened last night. I scarcely believe it myself." He dropped his eyes and bit his lip. "Last night I had a terrible toothache. It kept me awake. I heard the dogs barking outside. They made such a racket I went to the window to see what was wrong. There I saw a woman walking alone on the road. I couldn't believe my eyes. Like Moses at the Red Sea, she stretched out a stick, and the dogs stopped barking! All of them, every one. They stood still like soldiers in a row." He swallowed and took a deep breath. "I know it sounds crazy, but I swear it was Mara."

"My Mara?" Ilija asked, a chuckle in his voice. The smile on his face betrayed his disbelief.

"Yes, Ilija." Živadin wrung his hands. "My brothers laughed when I told them this morning. They said it was absurd, that I must have been drunk. They said I shouldn't embarrass myself by bothering you." His gaze dropped to the wooden floor again. Then looking up, he added emphatically, "I'm not crazy, Ilija. I must ask Mara. Whatever she says I'll believe. And I apologize in advance if I'm wrong."

Ilija smiled tolerantly, amused at Živadin's preposterous tale. What would his wife be doing on the road alone at that time of night? "You must be mistaken, Živadin," he replied. "Mara was with me and my boys until nine o'clock last night. The mill ran all night, so last night I slept here. It's peak season, you know. But," he chuckled, "I'm certain Mara was home asleep with the children."

Another heavily loaded wagon drew up to the platform, drawing Ilija's attention. "Mara should be here any minute to get some flour. You can ask her yourself. Now if you'll excuse me . . ." Ilija said and turned toward his customers.

A few minutes later, Mara came through the side door near the house, carrying an empty round wooden container. She was dressed in a navy-blue dress and dark stockings, the same outfit she had worn the night before. Wisps of brown hair curled from beneath the edge of her kerchief.

"Mara," Ilija called to her over his shoulder when he noticed her arrive, "Živadin wants to talk to you." He tilted his head toward Živadin, who started toward Mara.

Mara placed the container on the brick square beside the large wooden tub that held the family flour. Smiling sweetly, she watched Živadin approach.

His eyes darted back and forth, and he spoke in low tones. "Mara, this is very embarrassing. For the sake of my sanity, I have to ask you something." He clenched his hands until his fingertips turned red. "Around midnight last night I saw a woman walking on the road in front of my house. And . . . and it looked just like you, Mara." He stood back, as if to ward off a blow.

"Yes, Živadin, it was me," Mara answered straightforwardly.

Overhearing Mara's reply, Ilija dropped the sack he was lifting. He whirled around with a stunned look on his face and walked toward her.

"Ilija, I was going to tell you . . ." Mara's tone was apologetic. She turned to her husband. "I've been paying my tithe to the church—the 10 percent of income the Bible says belongs to God." She searched Ilija's face, his eyes, for a reaction. She realized how humiliating this might be for a man in his position. "I know you provide all my needs." She reached out and touched his arm. "But I have no spending money of my own. I want to be able to give my own tithe and offerings to God."

Ilija did not answer. He just stood and stared. Mara continued.

"Mila and I came up with a plan. We estimated my living expenses and the value of my work. We decided it would be fair for me to take about twenty-five pounds of flour from our bin twice a month and sell it. So every second Wednesday I take a sack to Mila's house. She sells it at half price to the poor and gives me the money. That's where I was going last night." Her last words dragged slowly.

When Mara finished, Ilija's brow was wrinkled and his eyes squinted, looking at her. "How long have you been doing this?" he asked in a subdued voice.

"About seven months," she replied, anticipating a reaction.

Ilija's mouth fell open again.

Mara turned to Živadin. "Last night when those dogs ran toward me, I nearly panicked. Then I remembered I was doing God's business. So I raised my stick and spoke to the dogs sternly. I said, 'Satan, you sent these dogs. In the name of Jesus, I command you dogs to stop barking!' And you know what? They did!" Her face lit up at the recollection, and when she turned to Ilija, she was smiling.

Živadin could not conceal his immense relief. His face beamed. "You are a holy woman, Mara. I feel like a new man. Now my brothers will believe me. I knew you'd tell the truth. I'm not crazy!" He shook her hand vigorously, then grabbed Ilija's hand, exclaiming, "Thank you! Thank you!" He almost danced out the door to the platform.

"Wonderful morning! Nice day!" His greetings to the waiting men feeding their horses outside floated back.

Ilija and Mara remained alone. "Mara, Mara, what am I going to do with you?" Ilija repeated, shaking his head. "You're a God-fearing woman, and I don't begrudge you helping the poor. Lord knows, we have more than we need." He paused and sighed. "But sometimes you embarrass me." They looked intently into each other's eyes without saying more.

Then Mara smiled her understanding, picked up her container, and began filling it with flour.

11
Surprising Outcomes

Saint Luke's Day, October 31, soon arrived—the day of Mara's birth family's patron saint. Leaving the children at home with Petra, and the mill under the supervision of a senior worker, Ilija and Mara climbed into a single horse-drawn carriage and set out for Mladen's house.

At the home where Mara had been born and where her father still lived with her two brothers and their families, they found old friends gathered to celebrate and feast. Mladen led Mara and Ilija to a seat at the table near the local Orthodox priest. The black-robed, white-haired man with snow-white beard and mustache was a distant relative and had taught Mara as a child. Seeing her again, his face lit up. Mladen and his wife, Marija, sat across from them.

Midway through the meal, Mladen, not wanting to waste any time, began. "*Popa* Jovan, my sister doesn't go to the Holy Orthodox Church anymore. She has become a Jew. She goes to church on Saturday. Can you straighten her out?"

Turning to Mara, the priest's wrinkled face looked troubled. "Mara, is this true? Have you truly abandoned the faith of your father and your people?" he asked earnestly.

Mara replied quickly. "No, *Popa* Jovan, I haven't abandoned my faith. I pray and read my Bible every day. I love God's Word." She tossed a glance at Mladen. "Yes, I go to church on Saturday like the Jews, but also like Christ and the first Christians."

"Oh, my daughter, you are in error," the kindly priest protested. "Jesus made Sunday sacred by His resurrection on that day. The first Christians worshiped on Sunday."

"There, Mara!" Mladen jumped in, newly confident. "I'll bet you can't find in the New Testament where it says they kept Saturday."

Because townspeople and relatives often asked Mara questions about her peculiar beliefs, she carried her Bible with her wherever she went. By now she had become adept at finding her way in its pages. Aiding her were verses underlined for emphasis and little slips of paper that peeked out from between pages marked for special attention. Holding her Bible now, Mara turned to Mark 6:2 and read the verse out loud. " 'And when the sabbath day was come, he began to teach in the synagogue.'

"It says here," Mara explained, "that Jesus went to the synagogue on Saturday. And the Bible says that He is our example." She turned to 1 Peter 2:21. " 'For even hereunto were ye called: because Christ also suffered for us, leaving us an example, that ye should follow his steps.' "

"Yes, Mara, but that was before His resurrection," the priest protested. "Afterward, the Christians kept Sunday."

"*Popa* Jovan, Sunday is the first day of the week. The Bible mentions it only a few times—and not once connects it to a worship service. I'll look the verses up. I have them underlined." She turned to one of the paper markers. " 'And upon the first day of the week, when the disciples came together to break bread, Paul preached unto them, ready to depart on the morrow; and continued his speech until midnight' [Acts 20:7].

"This verse says the disciples came together to eat before Paul departed on a trip the next day," Mara explained. "The Jews counted their days from sunset to sunset, so 'the first day of the week' is actually Saturday night after sunset. The verse says Paul spoke 'until midnight.' The believers had come together to see him off, not to worship," Mara said. "Another time the first day is mentioned is here, in First Corinthians chapter sixteen, verse two." She turned to another tab and read, " 'Upon the first day of the week let every one of you lay by him in store, as God hath prospered him, that there be no gatherings when I come.' This verse talks about putting money away at home. There's no worship service implied here. The text doesn't even mention a meeting."

Mara thumbed through her Bible. "There's another verse where Jesus appeared to the disciples after the Resurrection. Let's see. Here it is, in John chapter twenty, verse nineteen. 'Then the same day at evening, being the first day of the week, when the doors were shut where the disciples were assembled for fear of the Jews, came Jesus and stood in the midst, and saith unto them, Peace be unto you.' "

Mara had barely finished reading when Mladen broke in. "See, there, Mara. The disciples were meeting together on the first day. I knew it was somewhere in the Bible."

Mara looked unruffled. "Mladen, notice it was an evening meeting. The doors were shut. The disciples were afraid and hiding. It was not a church worship service." She turned to the priest. "I won't read the other first-day verses because you know them. They speak about the women at the tomb and the Resurrection."

Mladen slid down in his seat, his discomfort evident. He adjusted his shoulders and frowned. His wife listened. Ilija took everything in.

"Mara, Mara, you were my best student in school. I remember you never missed a Sunday liturgy. What has happened to you, my daughter?"

Mara smiled sweetly. "I've been studying my Bible, *Popa* Jovan, and I know many things I didn't know before. If Jesus changed Saturday to Sunday, then somewhere the Bible must tell us that. But it is not there."

"The apostle Paul said the law was nailed to the cross," the priest replied, taking another approach. "That means the law was destroyed."

"Yes, *Popa* Jovan, but it was the ceremonial law that was nailed to the cross, not the Ten Commandments." Mara continued talking, picking up steam as she went along. "People get confused. They don't know the difference. The Ten Commandments make up the moral law. It's eternal, like God. It tells us how to show our love toward Him and humanity. God wrote it on stone with His own finger. The ceremonial law was called the law of Moses. Moses wrote it in a book. It was temporary; it dealt with blood sacrifices for sins. When Jesus died, that law ended. That law was nailed to the cross. That's why when Jesus cried out 'It is finished!' the curtain in the Jewish temple was torn in two from top to bottom by an unseen and mighty hand. The Lamb of God was slain once and for all."

"But Mara, you know the Holy Orthodox Church goes back to the apostles. We have been in existence for millennia. How old is the church you go to now? How can it be the right church?"

"We are not saved by the church we belong to, but by our personal relationship with God, *Popa* Jovan. Many truths the first Christians believed became lost and forgotten over the years. Some so-called Christian beliefs actually came from paganism, and most Christians don't know that." Mara took a breath. "Yes, my church is less than a hundred years old, but it teaches strictly what the Bible says. God raised this church up with a special message to bring Christians back to the truths of the Bible, to prepare people for Jesus' soon second coming and the end of the world. Isaiah chapter fifty-eight, verse, twelve puts it this way." She opened her Bible again. " 'And they that shall be of thee shall build the old waste places: thou shalt raise up the foundations of many generations; and thou shalt be called, The repairer of the breach, The restorer of paths to dwell in.' "

The priest looked mystified. Mladen looked like he wished himself somewhere else. Mara, on the other hand, felt energized and elated. The feast had turned into a Bible study. Most conversations had halted, and as people ate quietly, they turned their ears to listen. When Mara looked about, she found eyes staring back at her. Ilija looked at Mladen, and Mladen at the priest—their eyes wide. Mara apparently knew what she was talking about. She was by no means finished. Turning back to the priest, she continued. "The apostle John says God made the world through Jesus. 'In the beginning was the Word, and the Word was with God, and the Word was God. He was in the beginning with God. All things were made through Him, and without Him nothing was made that was made.' [John 1:1–3].

"So if Jesus made everything, then He made the Sabbath also. And when He told the Pharisees He was Lord of the Sabbath [see Mark 2:27, 28], He was saying the seventh day is the Lord's day, Jesus' day. And if He made it, then it was He who rested on it and blessed it," Mara concluded. She closed her Bible, laid it on the table, and folded her hands in her lap.

"I know you love God, Mara," the elderly priest replied. "You're a good woman. Just keep praying. God will lead you."

Mara noticed that many of the guests had finished eating and were still listening. She had hardly touched her plate, yet her soul felt satisfied. For many this gathering became a turning point in their lives.

After dinner, several women, including Mladen's wife, Marija, sought out Mara with questions. For the first time in a long time, she noticed Ilija looking at her with pride and pleasure in his dark eyes. She had missed that look in recent months. Now it had returned. Mladen's *Slava* had turned into Mara's miracle.

One morning about a month later, while walking to the grain mill, Mara encountered a church member from a neighboring town. He was bringing his grain to the mill to be ground. "I saw Mladen's wife, Marija, in church last Sabbath," he told her. "Did you know she's been going there regularly?"

Mara's mouth fell open. "Why no. I didn't!" After he left, she thought about it. *If Marija is attending the Seventh-day-Adventist church nearest to her, that's a good six-mile walk.* Then she remembered Mladen's threats to evict anyone in his house who would leave their national church. *Oh, Marija,* Mara exclaimed to herself, filled with joy as well as dread, *what will happen to you?*

The next time Mara saw Mladen and Marija was in August when she and Ilija visited her brother's village for the local church's *Slava*. After the initial greetings, Marija pulled Mara to the side. "Mara, I have great news. Two of my daughters were baptized. First I was baptized, then they decided to join."

"Oh, Marija! That's wonderful! But what of Mladen? How is he taking this? I can't forget how furious he was with me."

"At first I didn't tell him I was going to the Adventist church. He assumed I went out to visit a neighbor. But when I got baptized and then our two daughters living at home joined me, we couldn't keep it a secret any longer. He had to know."

"And . . . what happened?"

"Oh, he fumed terribly for weeks. He wouldn't talk to us. He only grunted and slammed doors. Then when he did talk, he snarled. But it seems he's gotten over it now." Marija bent forward, chuckling. "What can he do? He's outnumbered!" Her face turned serious. "I want you to know, Mara, that Mladen is a changed man now. It's really a miracle."

"God is so good!" Mara exclaimed, wrapping Marija in a hug.

"I have more news yet. My four married daughters tell me they're going to be baptized, too. That makes all six girls. Only my son and Mladen remain." She waved her hand. "They don't have a chance. The church is praying for them!"

Mara's eyes sparkled. "Praise the Lord! What wonderful news. I was so worried about you. By the way, what does Petar say about all this?"

"Petar? Well, you remember how indifferent he was. He hasn't changed. It's all irrelevant to him. I suspect he told Mladen to let me alone."

Winter snows came and went, and before long, spring showers urged nature back to life. The farm produced abundantly, and the orchard hung heavy with fruit.

One peaceful July afternoon, the fields of winter wheat stretched to the horizon ripe for harvesting, their golden brown heads hanging heavily from their stems, when the wind suddenly picked up. The sky darkened and began to crackle.

"We need to go inside! It looks like a hail storm," Mihajlo shouted to the men working in the fields. They took cover in the family's common kitchen. Sitting helplessly inside, listening to the tempest rage and the thunder roar in rolling masses, they watched through the window as white lightning streaked through the dense blackness that enshrouded their vulnerable crop. Within half an hour, the winds began to subside, the darkness lifted, the sky cleared, and a beautiful rainbow appeared in the sky. When the family went outside to survey the damage, they beheld a miracle.

"It looks like the winds divided just before the storm hit our fields. They looped around and came together after passing us," Milorad observed, as the men stood amazed. "I've never seen anything like this!"

On the fields adjacent to theirs the wheat lay smashed to the ground, a few broken stems poking up where minutes earlier a forest of ripened grain had stood. Large hailstones covered the devastated fields like a thick white blanket. But the family's fields remained intact, the wheat stalks full.

From surrounding towns, people came to see and to marvel. Živadin, their neighbor, was among the first. For months afterwards, he related to anyone who would listen the story of Mara's midnight errand and the strange behavior of his watchdogs. "Mara's God saved their fields because Mara gives offerings to her church. She's faithful and generous and tells the truth," he would tell them.

To all who came, while Ilija looked on in wonder, Mara took out her Bible and read the promise that had been so dramatically fulfilled before their eyes: " 'Bring ye all the tithes into the storehouse, that there may be meat in mine house, and prove me now herewith, saith the Lord of hosts, if I will not open you the windows of heaven and pour you out a blessing, that there shall not be room enough to receive it. And I will rebuke the devourer for your sakes, and he shall not destroy the fruits of your ground; neither shall your vine cast her fruit before the time in the field, saith the Lord of hosts' " (Malachi 3:10, 11).

12
Family Reforms

Mara often found herself teaching others about the Bible. As a child, she had dreamed of becoming a teacher, but when she was unable to continue her studies after the fourth grade, she was forced to abandon her dream. Now, it seemed that her desire to teach was becoming more of a reality with each passing day. Whenever she discovered something new in her reading, she shared it with the family. And although she lived in a patriarchal society and knew her place as a woman, the men listened when she spoke with the authority of Holy Scripture.

One Sabbath, as the sun beamed down its warm rays, Mara was walking home with her children from the Uzveće Adventist Church when she ran into a neighbor who was sweeping pig droppings from the path in front of her house, gathering them into a pile to be used as fertilizer.

"Today's a big day, Mara!" the woman called out as Mara approached. She stopped sweeping and leaned on the broom handle.

"Why is that, my friend?" Mara inquired. Vera and Nata waited at her side, each holding one of the boys by the hand while they squirmed and poked the toes of their sandals into the dirt.

"Tonight my sons bring home their pay. Tomorrow I can buy some oil and cheese and bake some *gibanica* strudel," she explained happily. "My money jar's just about empty."

"I see," Mara responded. "Enjoy your baking." As she went on her way, she pondered what the woman had said. Mara knew that three of the woman's sons worked as day laborers on the Vitorovich farm and received a fair wage, but she also knew that the small piece of land the woman's family owned could not provide them with enough food for their needs. Land was gold; a person's wealth was judged by the size of his land holdings. This chance encounter reminded Mara that there were poor people all around her who were struggling to survive. An idea began to form in her mind.

That night after the children had gone to bed, she read and thought as she waited for Ilija to come in from the grain mill. He was bone tired when he arrived. Preparing for bed, Mara told him of her conversation with the neighbor, adding, "I read something today, Ilija." She picked up her Bible and turned to Deuteronomy 24:14, 15. " 'Thou shalt not oppress an hired servant that is poor and needy, whether he be of thy brethren, or of thy strangers that are in thy land within thy gates: At his day thou shalt give him his hire, neither shall the sun go down upon it; for he is poor, and setteth his heart upon it.' "

She closed the Bible. "We pay our workers every week on Saturday. But here it says we should pay them daily," she told her husband.

"Is that so?" Ilija said, half asleep. "Talk with Milorad in the morning. See what he thinks." He tumbled into bed.

The next day was Sunday. Farm workers had the day off, and only the extended family gathered for lunch. After the meal, Mara told Milorad about her conversation with the neighbor and read the verses in Deuteronomy that she had read to Ilija the night before. "These farm workers don't work every day, but they have to wait until the end of the week to get their pay. In between, they run out of money. Couldn't we pay them at the end of each day?"

Milorad thought a few moments, then glanced at Ilija. Ilija did not raise any objections. "We've never done that before," Milorad said slowly. "But I suppose we could try it."

On Monday, when the workers finished their evening meal and got up to leave, Milorad stood and made an announcement. "Don't go before collecting your day's wages." Surprised faces looked at each other, grinning, and the men immediately fell into a line.

Flanked on one side by his eldest son, who helped supervise the farm, and by Mara on the other, Milorad checked the records of hours worked and counted out the dinars for each man as he approached.

"Don't thank me. Thank Mara," he told the workers when they expressed appreciation. "She read in the Bible that we should do this."

Picking up their money, workers tipped their hats and smiled at Mara, thanking her and leaving happy. For them it proved to be a godsend.

Some time later, Mara got hold of some books that taught a healthy diet and lifestyle. Published originally in America, the books had been translated into Serbian and printed in Yugoslavia. Immediately after her baptism, Mara had asked that food for her and her children be set apart before any lard was added. She would not eat pork products because she believed them unfit for food. Instead of lard, she used sunflower oil. Earlier, she had encouraged the family to plant sunflowers in a patch of land. They constructed a press out of wood where they could press the ground-up sunflower seeds themselves.

"The Bible makes a difference between clean and unclean animals," Mara explained, when asked about this. "The unclean animals are not fit for food. God should know. He made them. In the Garden of Eden, God gave Adam and Eve fruits, grains, and nuts to eat. That's the perfect diet. But right after the Flood when there was nothing else, God allowed Noah to eat meat."

Some questioned further, claiming that the unclean animals were merely a Jewish ceremonial taboo. To these, Mara read God's instructions to Noah in Genesis 7:2. " 'Of every clean beast thou shalt take to thee by sevens, the male and his female: and of beasts that are not clean by two, the male and his female.' Noah knew the difference between clean and unclean animals," she pointed out, "and he lived a thousand years before the first Jew. So the distinction between clean and unclean animals isn't a Jewish law, but a health fact. God made us and knows what food suits our bodies best."

One of the things Mara learned from her reading was that greasy foods did not promote health. Because the family raised so many animals, meat provided a large portion of the diet, and it was usually fatty. People commonly believed that grease contributed to physical strength and endurance, that if you had some fat on you, you were strong and healthy. Lard was a staple in most cooking. Roasted young pig and lamb, grilled beef, and fattened smoked goose and duck were regular fare. "Even your doorknobs are greasy," a visiting pastor once observed.

Since coming home from a district conference in Šabac, Mara had become a vegetarian. She did not expect the family to follow her in this, but she did suggest they cut down on grease to improve their health.

Her books also stressed the nutritional benefits of whole-grain bread. The mill ground various grains in different degrees of refinement. Poorer people usually used the coarse unsifted flour containing all the bran. Using the entire kernel meant less waste. Some used corn flour for bread. Well-to-do people preferred the superfine sifted white flour. Bread, light and airy like a sponge, and standing high like spun cotton, was a status symbol. They used the white part of the kernel and fed the bran and germ to their animals.

"We're raising healthy hogs instead of healthy people," Mara lamented, trying to persuade Milorad to make a change. "We need to eat the whole grain just like it grows." When Mara's turn came to bake the weekly batch of bread, she decided to experiment. She had never made whole-grain bread before.

Early that morning, according to her customary procedure, she mixed and kneaded the dough, using the usual home-grown yeast from bran. She covered the dough in bowls with a cloth and set it out to rise. Then she waited.

"They're not rising," she observed, peeking under the cloths. She waited some more and looked again. "Still not high." Finally, she dumped the dough onto a board, punched it down, kneaded and shaped it into loaves, and covered the loaves for a second rising. Then she waited After waiting twice as long as normal, she slid the loaves into the brick oven to bake. "Maybe the heat will make them grow," she mumbled to herself.

When workers filed in for lunch that day, they saw flat loaves of dark bread on the tables, a sight that brought scowls to their faces and complaints to their lips. "Master Milorad, we eat this kind of bread at home. We want the rich man's bread! You're cheating us," they grumbled.

The family's reaction proved no better. "I'm sorry, Mara, but this bread is heavy as lead," Milorad moaned.

"It's a rock and flat like a pancake!" griped Mihajlo.

Ilija disapproved too. "I can understand cutting back on grease, but God can't possibly expect us to eat this stuff!" he protested, pointing sourly to the flat, dark mass.

The next day Mara baked another batch of bread, this time completely white. *I guess I can't expect to win every battle,* she thought. Taking the rejected bread from the day before, she soaked the thick loaves in leftover grease and threw them to the pigs. They attacked them with gusto, grunting their approval and fighting to seize their share. *Look at that. Sometimes animals are smarter than humans,* she reflected. Shaking her head, Mara continued to make small batches of whole grain-bread for herself and her children, who occasionally sneaked into the kitchen pantry to sample some of the fluffy bread when their mother was off duty.

On another occasion, Mara found Milorad sitting outside on a bench, enjoying the warm evening air and gazing up at the darkening heavens to watch the stars make their nightly appearance. All the brothers enjoyed looking at the stars. She sat down beside him.

"One day we'll see a little black cloud up there," she told him, pointing up to the sky. "It'll grow brighter and brighter and larger and larger until it shines brighter than the sun. It will be Jesus coming in glory with all His holy angels to take us home."

"You have a wonderful faith," Milorad replied. "It's a gift. I wish I could believe like you do." Noticing the Bible in her hand, he asked, "What is it, Mara? Do you have something to tell me?"

"I'd like to read you something." She opened her Bible to Galatians 3:28, which she had marked. " 'There is neither Jew nor Greek, there is neither bond nor free, there is neither male nor female: for ye are all one in Christ Jesus.' " Mara closed the Book and continued, "We feed our workers the same food that we eat, and we treat them good. But they sit at separate tables from the family. Never together. Society may put them in another class from us. But the Bible says we're all equal in God's eyes. What do you think about letting the workers sit with us?"

Milorad looked at her in surprise. "It's contrary to custom, for sure. We'd certainly shock our friends." He chuckled at the thought. "Let me think about it overnight, and I'll ask my brothers." The next day, he agreed.

When hungry workers filed in for lunch that day, Milorad made an announcement. "Sit anywhere you like today. We don't want you to separate yourselves from us. Under God, we're all equal."

Shy at first and awkward, the stunned workers required some encouragement before they found new seats and mingled with the family. Poor peasants sitting alongside landowners—it was a revolutionary move. More than one commented, "Wait till I tell my wife. She'll never believe this."

Word soon spread throughout the district. The Vitorovich family's employee relations became the talk of the town and beyond. Everyone in need of a job wanted to work for the family. They never lacked for help.

13
The Terrible Two

"Mother, we went to see Grandpa Svetozar today," Vera said. Svetozar was actually the children's great uncle, Jovan's brother, who lived with his wife, and two married sons and their families in the adjacent *zadruga*.

"You did?" Mara replied. "Did you have a nice visit, my pet?" Mara had started to make strudel dough for *gibanica* when Vera came into the kitchen. A barrel of wheat flour stood in the corner beside a wooden vat of salt and a jug of water on the table.

"My brothers showed them how to pray." Vera smiled and nodded her head, proudly.

"Oh, that was nice."

"Yes! Everybody was eating breakfast when we came. They gave us some French toast with sugar on it." She licked her lips, sucking in her lower lip. Mara sprinkled salt into the bowl of flour and added some water, listening as she kneaded the mixture with her fingers.

"My brothers knelt on the floor and prayed. They said everybody's names. I saw them peeking to be sure nobody got left out," Vera continued.

"Hmmm. Is that so?"

"Yes!" Vera skewed her mouth. "Then Voja forgot to mention Leposava. So Cveja jumped up and hit him on the head. Then he knelt down again."

"Oh?" Mara said in surprise, lifting her floured hands from the dough, her mouth open wide.

"Yes! Then Kata came in carrying oranges. Voja saw her, but Cveja forgot to say her name. So Voja got up and hit him over the head. He called him 'dummy.' " Vera kept nodding.

"Now, that wasn't nice at all." Mara shook her head.

"No! Then they knelt down again and prayed some more." Vera scratched her head, drawing her brows together. "I don't know why everybody laughed so hard. When we left I could hear them. Even after they shut the door." She cocked her head and paused. Then she nodded again, and her face brightened. "But they said we should come back and pray for them again soon."

A few months later, Cveja came down with a high fever and had difficulty breathing. His earlier bouts with diarrhea had set him back, and he did not rally quickly. Mara and Ilija took him to the doctor who had an office in Šabac.

"It's diphtheria," the doctor said after examining him. This second experience in a doctor's office left three-year-old Cveja wary of men in white lab coats and spectacles. He eyed him with suspicion.

"I'm going to give you something to make you well, my young man," the doctor said, preparing a hypodermic syringe. "It won't hurt, I promise. Now you're a brave boy, aren't you?" He inserted the needle into Cveja's backside.

But it did hurt. Cveja wailed. And a string of choice words poured out of his mouth, their meaning beyond his understanding.

"Where in the world did your little boy learn to talk like that?" the shocked and amused doctor asked Mara.

Red-faced, Mara apologized, wringing her hands. "Oh, Doctor, surely not at home. It's the grain mill. The boys hear the men talk. Their minds are like sponges. They pick up words. Believe me, I read them Bible stories and teach them to pray."

"No need to apologize, Mara, I know you," the doctor replied, still amused. "Bring him back in a week. This injection and the medication I give you should help."

He turned to Cveja. "Do you still hurt, my little man?" But Cveja had nothing more to say, so he turned his head to the wall.

Needless to say, within a week, Voja came down with diphtheria. He and his brother shared everything else; diphtheria would be no exception. Mara and Ilija took both their sons to the doctor—Cveja for his follow-up visit and Voja for initial treatment.

"How are my handsome twins?" the delighted doctor asked cheerfully when he saw the two brothers together, dressed alike in red pants and jackets. This time Voja had the high fever and did not feel like talking.

"Don't you hurt my brother with that big needle!" Cveja snapped at the doctor. He remembered his earlier visit and the shot. "I'll protect him!"

The doctor's face flushed in astonishment. He could not stifle a laugh. Turning to Mara and Ilija, he said, "This is marvelous! See how he loves his brother. You've given me something to tell my colleagues. There will be no charge today."

Still laughing, he whispered something to his nurse, who left the room, returning moments later with a red wooden truck, which she gave to Cveja. Taking him by his free hand, she led him out. The door had barely clicked closed behind her when the doctor administered the shot to Voja, and he let out a wail. But when Cveja returned with another wooden truck to give to his brother, more beautiful than any toys they owned, his crying stopped. The doctor let the boys take the toys home, and their adversary became an instant friend.

One day, about a month after the boys recovered from their illness, Ilija and Mara were working outside in the garden when they noticed a foul odor in the air. "What is that terrible smell?" Ilija asked, wrinkling his nose and sniffing the air. Recent rains had left pools of standing water in the fields where bellowing frogs collected. He set out to discover the source.

Following his nose, he spotted something in the grass. Upon closer inspection, it turned out to be a frog nailed to the ground. A short distance away he found another frog in the same condition. Pulling a rag from his pocket, he picked up the shriveled, smelly specimens.

"What did you do?" he asked his sons after finding them and confronting them with the evidence.

"We were just playing doctor," Cveja explained innocently.

"They were sick! We gave them injections, just like the doctor," Voja added.

"You didn't make them better," Ilija told them. "You made them dead. You can't do that anymore," he scolded.

Having nipped his sons' medical malpractice in the bud, Ilija dispensed one of the workers to clean up any remaining victims.

It had taken a while for Mara to purge her boys' vocabulary and teach them not to repeat words they did not understand, especially strange words they heard at the mill. "Those words might be naughty and hurt God's holy ears," she explained.

And so, newly cleansed of their defilement, the twins set out on a crusade. The reformed had seen the light and decided that others—willing or not—must see the light as well. One day when Mara went to the mill to see Ilija, her boys followed behind, and because she lingered a while, she witnessed them in action. A string of swear words coming from one corner of the mill drew the twins' attention. "You shouldn't use those bad words, you know!" they scolded, descending upon the men. "They hurt God's holy ears!"

"I'm sorry, I'm sorry! I'll never talk like that again!" one of the men replied defensively, putting up his hands and feigning remorse.

As the twins circulated through the mill where customers waited, conversations suddenly stopped. The sight of the two zealots approaching caused workers and customers to put forth their best behavior. Mara smiled to herself. *Who knows, my sons might grow up to be preachers some day*, she thought, *workers in God's vineyard*. She left to resume her work.

Having apparently rid the mill of profanity, the twins decided there were more vices to correct. Milorad had never smoked, and Ilija and Mihajlo had quit years before. If any of the younger men in the family smoked, they did so in secret. To smoke in the presence of their elders was considered disrespectful. Still, many customers at the mill smoked.

Remembering the words their mother had read from one of her church books about tobacco polluting the body temple where the Holy Spirit wants to live, the twins went forth armed with youthful fervor to convince every smoker they saw that he ought to quit. Mara chuckled as she watched her boys face the offenders. The encounters she did not personally witness Ilija told her about later. The boys stood hands on hips before the culprit caught in the act. He would obligingly pull his cigarette from his mouth, pretending to discard it, but in fact holding it behind his back. "I won't touch tobacco any more, I promise," he would declare. One man confessed later that because of the boys he actually did quit.

Another crusade completed. Another success. The twins went on to other things.

With all the activities on the farm, the twins, along with two of their younger cousins, found multiple ways of occupying the time. Often they observed the workings at the mill and the farm. During spring and summer months they watched the brick-making family who returned each year to work. In August, many of the fruits ripened and needed to be harvested.

To convert grapes into wine and plums into *šljivovica* (plum brandy), the fruit needed to be crushed. The smaller children, often joined by little local Roma friends, disappeared inside a vat, stomping and squealing with delight until the fruit turned into juicy pulp and their feet into purple wrinkles.

Before fermentation set in, Mara drew the fresh strained juice from the vat to fill several heated glass bottles. Corked and sealed with pitch, the bottles provided juice for her and her children. Mihajlo cooked the fermented fruit in the copper still. Every year a district business brought its truck and barrels and siphoned off a substantial portion of the brew to bottle and sell to local markets as well as to export to Hungary and Austria. Mihajlo retained a portion of the beverage for guests and family consumption. It was stored in barrels in the *čardak,* a special room at one end of a large building; at the other end the carriages and wagons were kept. In between the two rooms, an open staircase led to the loft where corn dried on racks.

Another day when Ilija came in tired, he reported to Mara on another of their sons' adventures. "Old Sima came by today with his flat-bed wagon, buying scrap iron," he told her. "Guess what your sons did?"

Mara lifted her brows, afraid to ask.

"You know how they like to dig in the fields," Ilija continued. "As usual, they found bits of metal, shells, bullets, even an empty cartridge left from the war. Anyway, it seems they wanted to sell it as scrap so they could buy you some colored thread for your sewing."

"Oh, how sweet," Mara said, smiling.

"Yes, well, wait till you hear the rest," Ilija retorted. "It seems they didn't have enough scrap metal, so they went to the smithy and got my largest sledge hammer. They sold it to Sima! Can you believe it? I can't imagine how they carried it. It must weigh eleven pounds." He shook his head. "Just as Sima was paying them for it, I looked out the mill window and spotted what was going on. So I came out and called to Sima. I had to buy back my own hammer!"

"They meant well, Ilija," Mara said.

"Sure they did. After Sima left, I let the boys know what I thought of their business dealings. I don't think they'll try that one again."

At a very early age, the twins had devised their own private language—Serbian spoken in reverse. The Serbian language written in Cyrillic is totally phonetic, with each character representing a single consistent sound. While still in their crib, they began by playing word games. Voja would challenge Cveja with a word to say in reverse before the count of ten, and then Cveja would do the same. When one succeeded, he scored a point. They began with easy one- and two-syllable words, eventually working up to longer ones as their vocabulary and skill increased. Whenever they did not want others to understand their conversation, they talked *natraške*, meaning "in reverse." They never found anyone else who understood.

In addition to speaking in reverse, the twins liked to pretend they spoke foreign languages. When winter came, customers waiting at the mill for their flour gathered in the boiler room that powered the machinery for the grain and saw mills. Here they kept warm. Cveja and Voja, always in identical outfits, were frequent visitors. When the man in charge, who stoked the steam boiler, saw them, he said, "Show the men how Ilija's sons speak foreign languages." *"Chumbily shlyika buka cheshan I tsogurina patka,"* Cveja would spout, proud of his made-up words.

"*Chorina guska,*" Voja would add.

"Look at that!" the men would exclaim each time, playing along. "How did they learn that? They're so young!"

And then the twins continued in their own backward language, which by then they could speak in long sentences. Though Vera tried desperately to decipher their words and master their language, she could not keep up. By the time she made out the first couple of words, they were into their next sentence.

When the men later spilled out of the boiler room, they told Ilija about his sons' visit. At home, Ilija shared the stories with Mara.

Day after day, when spring and summer came around, the twins watched their Uncle Mihajlo work on the farm, barefoot and in his usual work outfit—a white hemp shirt and pants woven by his wife, Lila. Cveja especially followed Mihajlo around, admiring his work grafting fruit-tree stock onto selected wild roots. Mihajlo basked in Cveja's praise, since his sons showed no particular interest in learning the skill.

In the *čardak,* barrels of various sizes contained anywhere between fifty-five and five hundred gallons of alcoholic beverages. Mihajlo alone knew exactly what each barrel held. One day when he went in to draw some *šljivovica,* Cveja watched him remove the bung on the flat end of the barrel that lay horizontally on a stand, and quickly insert one of the wooden faucets. Several sizes of faucets were stored in a box on a shelf. Unknown to Cveja, Mihajlo did this only when the barrel was half full, since he could not then siphon off the liquid from the top through a gourd.

"Mother, when will the fair come to town?" Cveja and Voja chorused one day in May when they were almost five. The highlight of village life was the annual *Slava* celebration of the local church. It was an event the children looked forward to all year long.

"Not for two months, children," she replied.

"How long is that?" they shot back.

"Not long. Before you know it, it'll be here."

A couple of weeks later, they wanted to know again, "Mother, how much longer is it until the fair?" And so it went.

During the fair, most children loved to ride the carousel, but on the twins' first ride, when they were three, they cried so hard the man had to stop the carousel so Mara could take her boys off. Ever since, instead of riding, they had just watched and listened to the music.

"Is it time for the fair yet?" The twins asked Mara again one day much later.

"Yes, children, it will be here tomorrow," she said, breathing a sigh of relief that the questions would soon end.

The day was young, and the twins needed something to occupy them. When two of their younger cousins came around, the four disappeared. A couple of hours later, Ilija and Milorad were carrying the boys home, unconscious.

"What happened? What's wrong with my boys?" Mara asked, running up to meet them.

"We found them in the *čardak* like this," Ilija said. "Actually Lila found them. The door was closed, and when she opened it, the fumes nearly knocked her down. All four children were lying on the floor unconscious in an inch of plum brandy."

Mara gasped; her hands flew to her face. "How could this happen?"

"It seems they pulled out the bung on one of the barrels and couldn't get the wooden faucet in. The pressure was too great," Ilija said. "It must have been full. The brandy ran out and the fumes must have knocked them out cold."

"Why don't they wake up, Ilija? Will they be all right?"

"Oh, I think so. They're drunk!" he said. "Once they sleep it off, they'll be OK."

The men carried the boys into the house. Mara changed them into clean dry clothes and put them to bed. All that night and through the next day, they slept. When they woke up the next night with a headache, the first thing they asked was, "Mother, when are we going to the fair?"

"I'm sorry, my children," Mara had to reply. "The fair came and went. You slept right through it."

Overwhelmed with disappointment, the twins broke down and wailed. Now they would have to wait a whole year before the fair returned. Sitting with them on their bed later, Mara read Proverbs 23:29–32, taking this opportunity to instill on their impressionable young minds the evils of alcohol. " 'Who hath woe? who hath sorrow? who hath contentions? who hath babbling? who hath wounds without cause? who hath redness of eyes? They that tarry long at the wine: they that go to seek mixed wine. Look not thou upon the wine when it is red, when it giveth his colour in the cup, when it moveth itself aright. At the last it biteth like a serpent, and stringeth like an adder.' "

Never again did the boys go anywhere near the *čardak* nor touch a drop of liquor when they grew up. By the next day, they had recovered from their stupor and their disappointment, and were out on the loose again.

One morning a few days later, Ilija came into the house to get a jar when Mara asked him, "Have you seen the boys?"

"They were walking toward the melon field behind the orchard a while ago. I saw Mihajlo there, picking watermelons."

Around noon that day, Petra came marching in, leading Cveja by the hand, with Voja and their two cousins walking sheepishly behind her. Mara noticed her frown.

"What did they do this time?" she asked in trepidation.

"Not much, only picked a couple dozen watermelon. Big ones, little ones, all sizes. Said they thought they were all ripe."

"I just did what Uncle Mihajlo does," Cveja tried to explain. "He thumped them. I did the same thing." Soon Mihajlo came by wheeling a cart full of watermelons. "There's more. This is only one load," he said, breathless. He had cut them and found all stages of green. "Don't be hard on the boys, Mara. Cveja was just trying to copy me."

That evening the pigs enjoyed a feast. But there was no watermelon for the twins for dinner that night.

"Oh, Lord. I asked You for a son and You blessed me with two," Mara prayed that night as she often did. "Help me now to know how to teach them. Protect them from harm and keep them safe. They seem to have such a knack for getting into trouble."

14
Leka Comes Home

When Leka turned twenty-one, she left her paternal grandparents and came to live with her mother. Mara had allowed her to remain in her grandparents' home until she came of age, hoping that Leka might receive her deceased father's inheritance because she was his only heir. But the court ruled that all paternal property remains within the parents' estate when they survive a son.

Mara and Ilija and the girls jubilantly received Leka, giving her the large room in the original house—the room in which the twins had been born. In her grandparents' *zadruga* there had been no small children, only four cousins who were close to her own age. So to Leka, her little brothers were like living toys, and she derived great pleasure from teasing them.

Voja, especially, reacted to her teasing, and for that reason she loved to pick on him. "Here, Voja, let me help you get dressed," she offered. When she did, she pinched his bottom. He jumped in protest, pulled off his shirt, and pulled down his pants. Leka exploded in laughter. "When I do that to Cveja, he just says 'Ouch!' " she chided him later, then apologized and promised never to do it again. But the next day the same thing happened.

Every Sabbath, Leka accompanied Mara and the children to church. Not long after arriving in Glušci, she was baptized in a nearby stream.

Several months later, Živan Borovich came calling. It was in his parents' modest home that the Sabbath-keeping group in Uzveće met. Several wealthy suitors had previously sought Leka's hand when she lived with her paternal grandparents. Despite the fact that most girls married before they turned twenty, Mara had encouraged Leka to wait, hoping she would marry someone from the church. In this young man, Mara saw a fine suitor for her daughter; in fact, unbeknown to Leka, Mara had invited him to visit!

While Živan, Leka, and Mara talked around a table at one end of Leka's room, five-year-old Voja entered through another door at the other end of the room where Mara's loom stood with a half-finished tapestry on it. As he often did for his mother, he busied himself turning the winch and rolling wool onto the shuttle. Mara noticed, but thought nothing of it. She sat back while Živan and Leka continued their conversation.

"How many horses does your family own, Živan?" Leka asked, among other things.

"We don't own any, Leka," he replied. "Some people boast about their carriages, some about their horses; we have nothing to boast of but the name of the Lord."

"Then how do you plow your land? Without animals to do the heavy work, how can you farm?"

"Well, sometimes we borrow a horse from my uncle. Sometimes we rent what we need. We have only five acres."

"Five acres," Leka repeated slowly, her voice subdued. "How can your family manage to live on that?"

"I know I'm a poor man, Leka, but I do have a trade. I'm a furrier."

After visiting for a while, Živan left. Mara and Leka remained at the table, discussing the young man's prospects as a husband.

"He's such a nice young man, Leka. He has a good character, and he's very responsible," Mara said. "Money isn't everything."

"I know," Leka replied. "But I've always lived comfortably. How can I get used to being poor now? His family has so little."

"That's true, my love," Mara replied. "But it's so important that your husband be a fine Christian. Živan even serves as an elder in the church."

Meanwhile at the other end of the room, Voja was turning the winch when the wool ran out. He kept turning so as not to call attention to himself. Mara glanced over and noticed. A minute later, Voja got up and left the room through the other door.

When Mara and Leka came into the communal kitchen several minutes later, they were greeted with wide grins and knowing glances. By then, everybody in the family knew the reason for Živan's visit.

"But how could you know?" Mara asked Lila. "It just happened."

"Voja came in a while ago," she said, laughing. "I had seen Živan Borovich arrive, and I asked Voja where he was. Voja said he'd tell me if—listen to this!—if I would brew him a cup of coffee!" She laughed again. "Imagine! Like he's a grown-up."

Mara's mouth dropped. "So that's what he was doing, the little rascal. Eavesdropping while pretending to work."

"Voja said you were trying to talk Leka into marrying Živan, but Leka wasn't sure she wanted to," Lila continued.

Živan and Leka did marry a few months later. Years afterwards, Leka would remember and tease Voja, saying, "If you tell me some gossip, I'll brew you a cup of coffee."

15
School Days

One sunny summer afternoon, while Cveja handed Mara items of laundry from her basket, Mara hung them on a rope stretched between two apple trees near the laundry room. Also hanging from the line was the bag containing the wooden clothes pins. Mara pushed it ahead of her as she continued hanging clothes to dry. Voja, meanwhile, sat on a rock nearby, looking at pictures in a book of fairy tales someone had given him.

As two men approached, Voja held up his book and began to recite the story out loud. He had not yet started school and could not read, but he pretended he could and made up the story as he went along.

"Your book is upside down," one of the men said brusquely as he passed by in a less-than-impressed manner. The other man smiled indulgently.

This was not the reaction Voja was expecting—or wanting. Most peasants witnessing such a display would marvel. "Look at that! Ilija's sons haven't yet gone to school and they can already read!" they would say. The twins would then take off laughing. This time, however, Voja hung his head and scowled. Mara watched him stomp off and quickly disappear.

In September 1936, the twins turned seven. It was time for them to start school, and they were eager to begin. "I got permission for you to attend the grade school in Uzveće," Ilija told them one day shortly before school started. "Glušci's school is at the other end of town. This one is less than a mile away, and you can easily walk there."

When the first day of school arrived, Mara dressed her boys in identical white long-sleeved linen shirts and brown britches that she had sewn herself and gave them last-minute instructions: "Now be sure to mind the teacher." Watching them trot off with Nata, now sixteen years old, she prayed, "Please, Lord, help my boys stay out of mischief and learn their lessons. This is their first adventure away from home."

School met six days a week, Monday through Saturday, from 8:00 A.M. to 1:00 P.M. Most Sabbath-keeping church members at that time did not think twice about sending their children to the mandatory grade school on Saturday. Their children attended the youth meetings with them on Sabbath afternoons, so they did not miss out on church. Later, however, under communism attitudes changed.

"Please, Lord, be with my boys," Mara prayed throughout the day as she worked. Though Nata had taken them to school, they would walk home on their own. Mara was working in her little garden near the house when the gate slammed shut and her boys called out to her.

"My children, come tell me how school went today," she said, standing up and wiping her hands on a rag. She gathered the twins on the steps of the house, where, brimming with excitement, they told her about their day. They shared a double desk in the front row; there were forty children in their class; the woman teacher who taught both first and second grades was nice; her fiancé's name was Voja, too; they liked school.

Mara nodded, listening and smiling. Each day upon returning home, the twins reported. From the beginning, they loved to learn, and their first year went well. Once they learned the Cyrillic alphabet, they could immediately read and write, and in the evenings they often practiced reading with their sisters.

Before long the school year came to a close. June 28, celebrated as Saint Vitus Day, was a national holiday commemorating the Battle of Kosovo as well as the last day of school. Classes were suspended, desks removed, and chairs put in place for parents to witness their children's performances—reciting poetry and singing the songs of Serbia. It was also the day to bring gifts to the teacher.

"I found a nice big rooster with a large red crest," Ilija announced, holding the big bird by its feet, which he had tied together so the twins could carry it. Mara and Ilija accompanied them, intending to stay for the program.

"Well, thank you," the teacher said graciously, untying the rooster's legs as Ilija held it. She placed it in a cage with the other farm animals brought by students as gifts. After the program, everyone set out for home and summer recess.

"This may be your school vacation, but there's no vacation from work," Ilija told his sons on their way home. "Tomorrow you start doing chores. The hogs need to be taken to pasture, the sheep tended, and wheat fields gleaned after harvest."

One hot summer day as the twins sat in the shade of a tree out in the fields, watching the sows root in the ground, the morning grew long, and their play distracted them from their chores. Suddenly, they looked up and the sows were gone. Hurrying home, they met their father at the gate.

"The sows were making a ruckus out here, and I let them in," he said. "What happened? Where have you been?"

"We were playing a game—and, and . . . the hogs got away," Cveja said, squirming.

"How come the hogs never get away when Vera watches them?" It was the last thing the boys wanted to hear. Vera was a girl, two years older, and she always did everything right.

"We'll be more careful next time," Voja promised tearfully after their father made clear his displeasure.

Summer passed quickly, and school resumed in September. The twins returned to the same classroom and teacher for their second year. Again, they did well and brought home good reports, making Mara and Ilija proud. When school let out for the next summer vacation, Ilija put the boys to work in the grain mill.

"Book learning has no value if you can't put it to practical use," he said. While Mara freely lavished praise on her boys—whether or not they deserved it—Ilija's compliments were scant.

The next year in September, eighteen-year-old Nata left home for missionary school in Zagreb. She had decided to get more education. The twins were promoted to third grade and transferred to the other classroom with Mr. Popovich, who taught both third and fourth grades.

During the year the teacher introduced the twins to geography, a new subject that fascinated them. At home, on their own initiative, they studied the geography of Europe and recited to all who would listen the capitals of each country in Europe that they had memorized. Before long, they memorized the populations of the capitals and the sizes of the countries in square kilometers.

The next September, the twins started fourth grade with the same teacher. It was 1939 and their final year of grade school.

On January 2, the family celebrated their *Slava* and invited Mr. Popovich, who was two years older than Leka. Nata returned from Zagreb for her two-week winter break. The family was together again, and the animated conversation turned to education.

"I didn't realize how important education is until I want back to school," Nata said. "Father, don't hold the boys back. Let them go on to high school."

"But Nata, they're just now old enough to be of help," Ilija countered. "One day these businesses will belong to their generation. How will they manage if they don't learn how to do so now?"

Mr. Popovich entered in the middle of the discussion. "Master Ilija, I understand your point, but Nata is right. Your sons are gifted. It would be a crime not to allow them to develop their minds." He paused. "I'm the only son of my father. My family was wealthy, too. If it weren't for my grade school teacher's intervention, I would not be a teacher today."

Ilija looked questioningly at the man and then turned to his boys. "Perhaps I could send the younger one." He looked at Cveja. "The older one can stay home and help me. Some families with several sons have educated the one who showed the most promise, while the others stayed home to work."

"Please don't separate them, Father," Nata pleaded. "Send both. They've always been together."

"Whatever is good for my brothers, that's what I think," Vera chimed in.

Mara smiled her agreement with her daughters, but did not intervene.

"Let me think about that, Mr. Popovich," Ilija said. "But I will agree to their taking the high school entrance exam. We'll see after they get their grades."

School let out the end of June. In July, Mihajlo drove the twins with his second son, Branko, to take the entrance test. Four years older than the twins and a mathematical genius, Branko had dropped out of school after a saw mill accident cut off four fingers of his right hand. For the past two years, he had been taking correspondence courses and now wanted to complete high school.

Immediately after completing the tests, the boys received their grades. Along with two other Uzveće students, Cveja and Voja passed. Branko also passed his examinations. All five students from Glušci who took the exam, including one of their cousins, failed. All these students had taken the test on the recommendation of their teacher, which meant that only four out of approximately seventy-five elementary school graduates from the two villages were eligible to enter high school. In the Kingdom of Yugoslavia, school standards were set very high.

"I guess you win," Ilija said, his attitude totally changed after hearing this report. "The twins can go to high school. But Šabac is too far for them to travel back and forth each day. Mara, we'll have to make living arrangements for the boys in Šabac."

16
Leaving Home

How will they survive? Can they manage by themselves? They're so young. Šabac is a big town. Will they remember what I taught them? Worries flooded Mara's mind as she scurried about at dawn, packing a large wooden trunk with feather pillows, goose-down comforters, bed and bath linens, towels, and identical sets of clothing for her precious sons. It was September 1940, and the twins had just turned eleven.

"We're up!" they chorused, also waking early. Leaving home at such a tender age didn't seem to distress them. Having a twin was like having another self. They were never alone. Young and invincible, they eagerly anticipated their newest adventure.

"Branko's trunk is already on board. I'll take the twins' trunk out," Ilija said, hauling the wooden trunk to the carriage he had earlier drawn up to the door. Fifteen-year-old Branko, the twins' cousin, was going with them. Excitement and anxiety bristled in the air as Ilija, Mara, and the three boys piled in.

Standing in the road outside the gate to see them off stood Mihajlo and Lila, Branko's parents. Nata had already returned to school in Zagreb. But Vera, sniffling and sobbing, waved a white handkerchief like a flag to her departing brothers as if surrendering them to a higher cause. "Goodbye! Goodbye. Good luck!" The cries followed the carriage as it rumbled off.

"Goodbye! Goodbye!" the boys shouted back, waving and craning their necks.

"*Srećno! Srećno!*" "Good luck!" villagers called out as the carriage clattered past them through Uzveće on its way to Šabac. Word had spread that the twins, the celebrities of Glušci, and the entire region, were going away to school. Dina, one of the Roma ladies, shouted her greetings. Her husband and two older sons worked for the family, and her younger sons had often played with the twins.

Before long, the carriage reached the streets of Šabac, paved smooth with flat stones that softened the clatter of its wheels. "Look at the automobile! See the army truck!" the twins shrieked, their heads twisting back and forth at the unusual sights on their first visit to the city. Multiple horse-drawn wagons, rows of storefronts crowded together on either side of the street, more people than they had ever seen before—all this gave them reason to gawk. Compared to Glušci, with its two thousand people, the district town of Šabac, with ten times that many residents, appeared huge.

"Look at the beautiful buildings!" the twins shouted as the carriage rumbled down the main street. "We never saw anything like this!" Besides the classic city hall and district court house, the town of Šabac boasted a new four-story hotel; a sleek, rounded marble bank building; four-year trade and business schools, a theater, two movie houses, three modern pharmacies, many shops; a library; a small Roman Catholic church; a large Serbian Orthodox church; and a Jewish synagogue. Except for small groups of Baptists and Seventh-day Adventists, Protestants were virtually unknown at the time. And since few Muslims lived in town, there was no mosque.

"Whoa, boys!" Ilija called to the horses, pulling back on the reins and stopping in front of a pastry shop. The gate of the courtyard next to it opened, and a short, stout, silver-haired woman emerged. "I've been waiting for you," she said, smiling. Mara had contacted the elderly widow, a member of the Šabac Seventh-day Adventist Church, who agreed to board the boys during the school year.

"*Tetka* Radosava, these are our sons and this is our nephew, Branko," Mara introduced the boys. Then spotting a large building diagonally across the street, she asked, "Is that the district high school?"

"Yes," the woman nodded. "It's very convenient, I must say." She opened the other wing of the eight-foot-wide gate so that Ilija could drive the carriage into the cobblestone courtyard. "My apartment is way in the back. The three boys will occupy one of the two rooms that I rent out adjacent to mine."

While the boys helped Ilija carry the trunks in, Mara hung up the two identical outfits, custom-made by a local tailor from soft brown woolen fabric with jackets decorated in braid. They were the twins' first store-bought outfits. "Remember, these are for church," Mara directed. "Now that you're growing up so fast and living in the big city, you need to dress like city folk." After unpacking, the five went shopping.

The sign on the store read *"BATA,"* and the twins ran in ahead. They emerged a short while later, each carrying a box. "Our first store-bought shoes!" the twins exclaimed proudly. Heretofore, they had either gone barefoot or worn their *opanke* sandals. Branko also bought a pair of shoes.

At the book store, the boys obtained their books and school caps with a tab designating their class. Then they returned to the house.

After settling the boys in, Mara and Ilija chatted with *Tetka* Radosava and then prepared to leave. "Now, be sure you obey *Tetka* Radosava, and help her with chores and firewood," Mara instructed. "Every Friday we'll come to pick up your laundry. We'll bring food from the farm for her to cook, and money for you for the next week."

She planted a kiss on each of their foreheads. "And remember, children, don't miss church. The Šabac group will be new to you, but you'll make friends. And since you're in school Sabbath morning, be sure to go to the youth meeting in the afternoon. Sunday, too."

"Everybody goes to the youth meeting Sabbath afternoon. It's not only for young people," *Tetka* Radosava added. "Sunday is for members to bring their friends."

Shadows of evening wrapped the courtyard in shade as the sun dropped to the horizon and the three boys followed Mara and Ilija out to the carriage. Climbing in, Mara turned for a last look at her sons.

"My heart aches already," she moaned under her breath. Then she and Ilija rode away alone, carrying two empty trunks home.

Each Friday Mara visited, sometimes with Ilija or Vera, sometimes alone. When Vera came, she gushed and giggled and chattered with joy to see her brothers. Nata remained in Zagreb. One Friday, however, Mara did not show up; she came on Sunday instead. She found Cveja in church, but Voja was nowhere to be seen. "Where is your brother?" she asked her younger son.

"I don't know, Mother." He shrugged his shoulders. "We were walking together to church when we saw a big circus tent at the crossroads. The sign said 'Belgrade Circus.' " Cveja paused. "Voja stopped to watch a ventriloquist for a few minutes, but he said he'd catch up later."

Mara's heart sank. *Just a few weeks away from home, and Voja has already disobeyed,* she lamented to herself. *Why is it that Cveja more easily complies? What will become of my firstborn with his fun-loving tendencies?* Stepping into her carriage, she drove away in search of the circus. She found the tent a short while later and stopped. A group of curious observers had gathered around a ventriloquist in a colorful suit who stood in front of the tent's opening, manipulating puppets and inviting people in. Mara drew closer. She squeezed between those standing in front of her to peer into the tent. There on a bench near the stage sat her delinquent son. He was turning his head and looking around, appearing impatient for the show to start. Suddenly, he looked back and saw his mother, eyes focused on him! His face grew dark, but he looked past and pretended not to see her.

"Voja," she called to him after waiting a few moments. *How did he get in?* she wondered. *It must be expensive. Where did he get the money?* He looked away, pretending not to hear her call.

"Voja," she called again, louder this time. Again, he ignored her. Sitting next to him, a woman with a small child threw a glance over her shoulder at Mara and then at Voja. He stamped his feet, jumped up, and stomped all the way out of the tent toward Mara. Just then, the ventriloquist moved his paraphernalia inside. The entrance flap came down. Voja stood outside, his face beet red.

"So, what do you want?" he asked, his voice breaking, almost in tears.

The words *"a soft answer turns away wrath"* from the Bible popped into Mara's mind. "Dear heart," she began, breathing a quick prayer and smiling, "last Friday your father and I couldn't come, so I came today." Her voice sounded low and mellow. "I left food at *Tetka* Radosava's place. Then I went to church. Cveja was there, and I gave him some pocket money. So, *Vojcika* [her pet name for him], Mother just came to see you and give you some pocket change too." She pressed a few coins into his hand and kissed him on the forehead.

"Goodbye, my dear son, my full house, my pet. God bless you," she said, and turned toward the carriage, her heart trembling. *He's in Your hands now, Lord. Keep him from straying from Your path,* she prayed earnestly. Without looking back, she climbed aboard, took up the reins, and drove silently away.

17
Rumors and Winds of War

While the twins studied in Šabac and their family went about their usual seasonal routines in Glušci, events on the world stage grew increasingly ominous.

When World War I had ended in 1918, the results included the dissolution of four ancient empires, the emergence of new independent states, and a totally redrawn map of Europe. Though Austria had blamed Serbia for the assassination of Archduke Ferdinand that had sparked the war, the victorious Allies held Germany chiefly responsible for the conflict. Forced to pay reparations, Germany couldn't maintain payments; its ailing economy collapsed. And from the rubble, Hitler ascended to absolute power.

Although most of the war-weary nations of Europe allowed their military defenses to decline during the 1930s, three nations had begun to make military moves—Hirohito's Japan in Asia and the Pacific, Mussolini's Italy in Mediterranean Africa, and Hitler's Germany in central Europe. In 1934, the consequences were felt in the Kingdom of Yugoslavia.

On October 9, 1934, Branko had come home from grade school early with shocking news. "School closed today. Our King Alexander was assassinated in Marseilles while on a state visit." The report of the tragic incident issued by the Yugoslav government stated simply that the deed was done by "an enemy hand," and no retaliation took place.

In 1938 an appeasing Europe had watched Hitler annex Austria and seize Czechoslovakia. But when Germany emerged as the mightiest modern fighting machine ever assembled and attacked Poland, the world suddenly awoke to a terrifying reality. Hitler's forces launched a blitzkrieg across Europe, toppling unsuspecting and unprepared countries in its path. And World War II erupted.

In Glušci, too, times had changed. Some of the younger family members wanted more independence, so in 1938 the Vitorovich *zadruga* had split in two. Milorad, who had the most sons, separated from Ilija and Mihajlo. Three years later, Ilija and Mihajlo had split. They divided property and animals among the three brothers according to the number of their sons. A wooden fence separated each of their three properties. Though independent, they shared farm equipment and remained on the same good terms.

In the interim, Milosav's widow had remarried and moved away, leaving her son behind with Ilija. Now grown up and married, he inherited his father's share. One of Milorad's sons, the only one to have completed high school, moved to another town to work as chief engineer at the railroad station.

Electricity had not yet come to the village, but almost every family owned a battery-operated radio. "Have you heard the news? Strange things are happening," town folks whispered among themselves. Everyone in Glušci had heard the alarming reports of hostilities in other parts of the globe. But in February 1941, peace reigned in the Kingdom of Yugoslavia.

Spring approached, and Mara started her seeds, dried from last year's crop, in wooden boxes kept inside the house near sunny windows. The men began preparing their fields for planting. Life continued, and though rumbles of war echoed in the distance, its reality seemed far away. In the evenings, families gathered around their radios to hear news reports of worsening world events. But dramatic events were beginning to occur locally as well.

On March 25, 1941, in Belgrade, thousands of citizens took to the streets to protest the secret signing of the Tri-Partite Pact with Nazi

Germany by Prince Regent Paul, who came to the throne after King Alexander's death. Surrounded now by Axis countries and with a million Italian and Nazi troops and tanks at its borders, the pact promised Yugoslavia neutrality, but it also allowed German troops to pass through the country. A military coup two days later dethroned Paul, set young King Peter on the throne, and disavowed the pact. The Serbs had defied Hitler. It was the first Balkan nation to do so. Far-reaching ramifications followed.

Shortly thereafter, as Ilija worked in the fields and Mara planted seedlings in her garden near the side of the house, a neighbor came through the gate.

"Mara, did you hear the news? Belgrade has declared a state of war. The government expects Germany to attack any minute. I just came from Šabac. The schools are closing and sending students home."

Mara stood up, alarmed. "Our boys. We must go for our boys." She carried the news to the men, and before long, Ilija was on his way to Šabac with two empty trunks to bring his sons and Branko home.

At Radosava's house, the twins waited with Radosava until Ilija arrived. "The school told us this morning, Father," the twins said. "We've already gathered our things." They showed him their folded clothes and belongings piled on the bed.

"I came as soon as I heard," Ilija said. He had drawn the carriage up to the house and went out to bring in the trunk.

After bidding goodbye to Radosava, the boys climbed into the carriage. Branko had moved in with another family two blocks away, so Ilija and the boys rode there to pick him up. Riding back to Glušci, they hardly spoke.

Arriving home, the boys found their beloved Nata. She had returned home from Zagreb a few days before. The political situation there had changed drastically, and strange things were blowing in the wind. All the Serbian students had been advised to leave while they could. Nata had departed by train the day after the announcement, just days before Croatia closed its border.

Within a week, mobilization notices arrived in the mail. The time had come for the present generation of men to march off to war as their fathers and grandfathers had done before them. The current peaceful interlude had come to an end.

Milorad's three sons, Mihajlo's older son, as well as Milosav's son— all left for Šabac to report for military duty. Mihajlo's oldest son had already served a term in the cavalry immediately after marrying, and when he left, he took one of the horses with him as required. War had come home again. Family members said their uncertain and tearful goodbyes.

18
Enemy Attack

"They're beautiful!" the twins exclaimed, surveying the array of colorfully dyed and decorated eggs the women and girls had designed. Despite the war, the family was preparing for the Orthodox Easter celebration at the church. In the afternoon, on Easter Sunday, the church grounds would resound with the music of Roma violins and accordions, folk dancing, and the happy laughter of children knocking their decorated hard-boiled eggs against those of their friends to see whose would withstand cracking the longest.

Mara said nothing, but her thoughts resounded loudly in her mind. *Eggs. What do they have to do with Christ's resurrection? The Resurrection is the hope of every Christian, yet fertility symbols gain more notice.*

On April 6, 1941, Palm Sunday by the Gregorian calendar, Ilija prepared to go to church for the special liturgy. Mara had risen early and was reading her Bible when an urgent knock sounded at the door. Milorad stood there, dressed for church in his braided vest and britches, his face grim.

"Mara, Ilija," he said. "I just heard the report. German planes bombed Belgrade. It happened at dawn this morning. They flew in at rooftop level and left the city in flames. Thousands of casualties are expected. Bombs are still falling."

"The heathens, how could they?" Ilija retorted, anger in his voice. "Hitler knows Belgrade is an open city. It was undefended!"

94

The family ate lunch later that day in a quiet, somber mood, listening to further updates on the radio. Days later, bombs were still falling over the city, and the radio reported, "Under cover of continued bombings, the combined Axis armies surrounded the Kingdom of Yugoslavia and attacked from all sides. The Yugoslav army has been cut off."

Our loved ones, what happened to them? Did they survive? The questions gripped every heart. Five of their own had gone off to war, not to mention Živan, Leka's husband.

"The Yugoslav army has collapsed. The country has capitulated," news reports confirmed a week later. Axis powers were cutting up the country like a cake, each taking the portions they coveted.

"Hitler has created a Greater Croatian State. He has annexed Bosnia-Hercegovina and surrounding areas to the Croatian province," further newscasts declared. "Croatia has announced its independence and declared war on the Allies." While the Independent State of Croatia followed Nazi policies, Serbia, where anti-Nazi sentiment was strongest, was occupied by the Germans.

Soon the Royal Yugoslav soldiers who had gone to war returned to their homes, carrying a strange report. "Our equipment wouldn't work. Canon balls turned out to be blanks. Guns didn't fire. Fifth columnists betrayed the army and sabotaged the equipment. In the confusion, the army dissolved without getting a chance to fight. Thousands of soldiers escaped to the mountains to pursue guerilla warfare."

But Živan, Leka's husband, had vanished. The family later learned that the Germans had taken him prisoner, but no one knew his whereabouts or whether he was still alive.

"The German military command has set up headquarters in the district courthouse in Šabac," Johann told Ilija one day. He spoke German fluently and often eavesdropped on German conversations when he traveled to Šabac. "Tomorrow they'll come through Glušci. It would be a good idea to display white cloths as a peaceful gesture."

Later that day, Mara fastened large, light-weight towels to poles Ilija had fashioned at the sawmill, then attached these to the wooden fence in front of their house. The next day, before noon, when German vehicles thundered through the village, no crowds lined the streets to welcome them. White sheets draped fences, and white towels waved like flags in mute witness of their unwelcome arrival and the reluctant surrender of the populace. "Just look at them, parading through our streets," Ilija murmured, as he and Mara watched through curtained windows.

"School will resume on Monday so students may complete the last school year," a messenger from town hall advised the residents, going from house to house one day in May. On Sunday, Mara bid her boys a reluctant goodbye. "Everything will pass, and the Lord will come," she encouraged them as well as herself. It was her oft-repeated phrase. "Please, Lord, keep my boys safe," she prayed. While the twins left for Šabac, Nata and Vera remained home with their parents.

"Hitler's combined Axis armies have plunged into Russia, four weeks later than originally planned," news reports declared in June of 1941. "In a speech given just before the invasion, Hitler blamed the delay on the Serbs whose coup forced him to divert vital resources to Serbia. The infuriated Fuhrer vowed to punish the Serbs and crush them mercilessly."

"Things don't look good," Mara said to Ilija after listening to the news report.

"Hitler never forgave us for helping bring down the Austrian Empire. Now he's determined to finish us off," Ilija replied, his face grim.

While the motorized German armies made swift progress in Russia, forcing back the unprepared Red armies, in Yugoslavia, just days after the invasion, resistance groups were beginning to mushroom. The first group, the Partisans, had organized in the Glušci region. Officers of the defunct Royal Yugoslav army, who had escaped rather than return home, organized Chetnik resistance fighters, loyal to the king. Many rallied to one or another of these groups. Guerilla warfare—it was how the Serbs had opposed their invaders throughout centuries of occupation.

"Have you seen Draga and his brothers lately?" Mara asked Ilija one day. "I pass by their house, and they're never around."

"I expect they've joined the Partisans," Ilija replied. "A number of our neighbors seem to have disappeared, young men and old—women, too. They're probably hiding in the mountains somewhere."

Many had indeed fled to the mountains, but in the flat fertile plains around Glušci, Draga and his two brothers were living in underground rooms and tunnels dug on their own land and camouflaged above ground with stacks of straw. Two-way radio enabled contact with comrades. At night they surfaced to get food from their families and conduct reprisals and sabotage missions.

War had come to Glušci, and danger lurked at every turn.

19
Captured

Bang! Bang! Bang! Someone was pounding on the door. It was noon, and Ilija, Mara, and the children had just sat down to eat in their own kitchen, which had been added on to their house after the *zadruga* had split. When Ilija opened the door, four German soldiers burst in, heavily armed. Black swastikas in a disc of white emblazoned the red bands on their left arms. Two of the soldiers pointed machine guns at the terrified family who cringed at the table. The other two pushed past Ilija, pistols drawn, and scattered throughout the rooms. No one dared say a word.

"Niemand gefunden!" the two said, returning empty-handed. They seized Ilija, who was the only adult male in the house. Since school had not yet begun, the twins were still home. Luckily for them, they were only twelve years old.

"Kommen Sie mit uns! Kommen Sie mit uns!" the soldiers shouted sharply. "Take food for three days!" they ordered in German. Having heard Yiddish in Budapest, Ilija understood the German and translated to Mara. Trembling, she grabbed some cheese, meat, a loaf of bread, and a bottle filled with water, put them in a canvas bag, and handed it to Ilija. He pulled the straps over his shoulder.

"Gehe! Gehe!" the soldiers shouted and shoved him toward the door. He turned and took a last long look at his wife and children. Helpless and horrified, they watched in silence.

The moment the door banged shut, the children dashed to the windows. Mara followed. The house was elevated, and the windows looked over the fence into the road. Peering through the thin curtains, they saw a long convoy of canvas-covered trucks; soldiers herded Ilija toward a group of men who stood behind one of the trucks.

"There's Uncle Milorad!" Cveja shouted, recognizing him in the group.

"And his three sons," Mara said, gasping in horror. "They must have stopped first at their house." Now Ilija joined them. The men followed behind one of the troop trucks as the convoy started to move away.

Pale-faced, the five onlookers watched the procession move up the street—first the troop truck, then a group of men walking behind it, then a motorcycle combination carrying three German soldiers, two armed with machine guns. Behind them followed another troop truck, another motorcycle combination, and so on down the line.

When the convoy had moved a safe distance, Mara pulled aside the curtain, pushed open the casement window, and poked out her head. The convoy had stopped at Mihajlo's house. The children craned their necks to see. Soon Mihajlo and his adult son were herded out, joining the group of men. Mara and her children continued to follow the convoy with their eyes until it reached Milosav's son's house, where they saw him being hauled off.

"Mother, where are they going? What will happen to them?" the children cried, pulling their heads back inside the room, their faces drawn and pale.

"I don't know, children, but God knows. We will ask His angels to watch over them. Let's pray." As she fell to her knees, the children gathered around, hands folded, eyes closed. "Merciful Father, Mighty Lord, You see Ilija and the others being taken away, we know not where. Surround them with Your mighty angels to protect them and return them to us unharmed. In the precious name of Jesus, we pray."

"Amen," the children chorused.

Soon the convoy disappeared, and women poured into the street from houses left empty of men. Underage children ran out with them. Collecting in groups, they cried and wailed, all talking at the same time. Seeing Mara, a few edged toward her. "Mara, Mara, what will we do?

Merciful heavens! Our men, our sons! They've taken them away! What if they kill them?"

"They're in God's hands," Mara could only reply, her heart heavy. "All we can do is pray. We must be strong."

For three long, heart-rending days there was no word. The mill motor remained silent; the fields were left untended; the saw mill was unused. All Glušci's able-bodied men had been captured and taken away. No customers brought grain to the mill. No one worked the farms. Even Johann had disappeared.

"The convoy came through Uzveće, too," Mila told Mara when next she saw her. "All our menfolk were taken. Except for women and children, there's no one left." In the men's absence, women, girls, and children tried to fill in where they could, milking the cows, caring for animals, doing the most urgent work. Anxious and desperate, they all hoped for some good news. Some inquired, but no one knew of the men's whereabouts or even if they were alive. On the third day Johann suddenly showed up at Mara's door.

"Johann! Where have you been? How did you get here? What happened to our men? Have you seen Ilija?" Mara bombarded him with questions.

"The Germans took us all to Šabac," he reported. "They released me when they realized I was German." He paused. "I saw Milorad and Mihajlo and their sons. They're in the military camp with the others, surrounded by barbed wire."

"And Ilija? Did you see Ilija?" she asked, her voice weak. Johann had not mentioned his name, and she feared the worse.

"No, Mara, I didn't," he replied slowly. "Seems he's the only one missing. I'm sorry, Mara." For a moment, he lowered his eyes. "But I'll keep checking and let you know what I find."

All the next week Mara prayed without ceasing, hoping for word. When Johann returned, his face looked grim. "I've tried everything I know, Mara. There's just no trace of Ilija," he conceded sadly, shaking his head.

In the days that followed, Mara carried on without saying anything to the children about their father's situation. *I know you're alive, Ilija,* she spoke in her heart. *Soon I'll hear some word about you. Thank You, Lord, I know You're taking care of my Ilija. Almighty God, You're in control.*

Three days later, Johann appeared again. "Mara, I have great news! I saw Ilija. He's in the military camp with his brothers in Šabac. The last ten days he's been sick, but he's OK now."

"Thank You! Thank You, Lord! I knew You'd keep him safe," Mara exclaimed. "What happened, Johann? Did he say?"

"Yes, Mara. All this time he's been in a hospital near the train station on the Croatian side. When the men were crossing the pontoon bridge over the Sava into what's now Croatia, he fell. They had been running behind the convoy truck, and he must have felt weak. They had not had water all day. His brothers ahead of him heard a rifle shot and turned back. They saw him lying on the bridge with one of the Ustashe soldiers standing over him, his rifle lowered. Milorad's son ran back to help Ilija, but another Ustashe charged him with his bayonet. He dodged, and the blade grazed his forehead. The soldier ordered him to go back and catch up with the others. That was the last they saw of Ilija. Actually, I knew about this when I first talked with you, Mara," Johann confessed, "but I didn't have the heart to tell you. Now I know the rest. Ilija told me himself."

"Tell me, Johann. What happened next?" Mara's eyes were wide.

"The bullet missed Ilija and lodged in the wooden bridge. But while he lay there, he heard two other soldiers speaking in Hungarian, which he could understand. So he spoke to them in Hungarian. One of the soldiers was an officer and very kind, Ilija told me. The officer asked him how he came to speak Magyarol. Ilija told him of his experience in Budapest in World War I. Anyway, the officer had him taken to the hospital and even visited him while he was there. Then when Ilija felt better, the officer directed someone to drive him to Šabac. It's amazing. He's our enemy!"

"Amazing? Yes. But God is the One who is truly amazing!" Mara replied. "I'm so relieved. Thank you, Johann. If you see Ilija again, tell him the children and I have been praying for him."

Johann smiled and left. The next day Mara saw him again.

"The Germans are trying to induce one of the Glušci men to accuse his neighbors of being Communists," Johann reported. "They want an excuse to execute them. So far, though, nobody has stepped forward. I just came back from Šabac. I don't know how long they'll keep them."

Finally, six weeks after rounding up the men and failing to force a betrayal, the Germans released the Glušci men and sent them home.

One hundred twenty of the men from Uzveće, however, never did see home again. The ones that came back reported. "One of our group gave in to the enemy. He accused a number of his friends of being Communists. We know they're not. All one hundred and twenty men he named were led away and disappeared."

Many homes in Uzveće were left to grieve and speculate on the fate of their loved ones. From one house a father and three sons had been taken; from another, a father and two sons; four brothers from yet another house, and so on. In the days and months that followed, their families clung desperately to hope. "Maybe they're in German work camps and still alive," they said. But time went on, and no letters came in the mail.

In the meantime, each new dawn bred uncertainty as the occupation continued, and during the night the unexpected often happened.

20
Enemy Occupation

"Be sure to mind *Baka* [grandma] Anka," Mara instructed her boys as they prepared to leave home for their second year of high school. "And remember the things I told you."

It was September 1941. *Tetka* Radosava had fallen ill with cancer and died, and Mara had arranged for her boys to board with another elderly widow who lived farther away but still within a mile of the school. The large kitchen of her two-room apartment would double as the twins' bedroom.

In December 1941, America entered the war on the side of the Allies. Fighting continued across the globe. By June 1942, more than a million Jews in Europe had been exterminated in the Nazi attempt to wipe the race from the continent. In the Independent State of Croatia, hundreds of Serbs and Romas who lived within its expanded borders shared the same fate in the extermination camp of Jasenovac.

Like others who protected Jews in countries over which the red flag with the crooked cross waved, the people in German-occupied Serbia could not be coerced into turning in their Jewish neighbors. The lives of many of these brave protectors were snuffed out.

"There are no books this year," the twins reported to their parents when they visited them in Šabac. "We have to take notes in class if we want to study." With printing presses down and paper hard to come by, everything was limited and in short supply.

"Why must we study German?" the twins protested to their mother on another visit. "They're our enemy. We don't want to speak their language." It was a sentiment shared by all the students though German, French, and Latin were mandatory in their curriculum.

"Now children, you must make a difference between the German language and politics," Mara counseled. "Not all Germans are in favor of this war. Study the language and do your best. You never know when you might need it."

One day Mara was working in her garden when she heard a strange sound. *What is that noise?* she wondered. She heard a faint drone like a swarm of bees, then the noise became louder, a deep thunder, followed by the ear-piercing shriek of sirens and a loud boom. "German planes!" she cried out, looking up. She ran into the house and watched through the window.

German *stukas,* flying low, were bombing something in the distance. The sounds of the planes diving, dropping their lethal cargo, then roaring back into the sky one after another, made her blood curdle. Parts of Glušci, too, suffered damage on that raid.

"Maybe we can hear the news tonight," Ilija said, later that evening. He pulled their radio—now forbidden—out of hiding. "At this time of night, radio frequencies may be clear enough to hear." German interference often obliterated BBC and Voice of America transmissions. Other than these sources, the only reliable information about the war came from an occasional underground newspaper smuggled in from Šabac or Belgrade that made its rounds from one home to another bearing news to readers eager to hear of Allied progress.

"Voja, Mother brought you a surprise," Mara said to her son on another visit to Šabac. "It's a guitar. Would you like to try it?" She handed him an acoustical guitar she had bought in Šabac. "When you learn to play it, you can participate in young people's meeting. Wouldn't you like that?" Her older son sometimes needed a little prodding.

Voja took the guitar and strummed it with his fingers. "It has a good sound. Thanks, Mother." His interest thrilled Mara's heart. But there were other distractions to be discovered in the city.

"The local soccer team has a game this Sunday afternoon at two o'clock," Voja excitedly informed Cveja. "Voja, Rojic, their best forward, will be playing." Rojic was Voja's idol. Both twins were ardent fans of the sport.

"We're supposed to be in church then," Cveja replied.

"I can never have any fun!" Voja exclaimed. Though he went to church every Sabbath afternoon, sometimes Voja succumbed to temptation on Sunday.

School days continued, and before long, winter's icy winds made travel difficult. When inclement weather prevented Mara from visiting the twins on Friday, she came on Sunday. Eventually spring crept in, the school year drew to an end, and the twins returned home for summer vacation.

"The sky looks like a painting on canvas," Mara mused one day, surveying the white cumulus clouds and the fields across the road turning green with clover. "War seems like a bad dream." But war did not vanish like dew in the morning sun. Some days it appeared less obtrusive. Yet always and in sundry ways, the enemy's presence hung over the land like a shroud. The threat of sudden retribution or a surprise strike lurked in every shadow.

"Some trucks just pulled up outside," Nata told her mother, glancing out the window. "German trucks." A few minutes later, they heard pounding and shouting at the door of the house. When Mara opened it, four armed soldiers burst in.

"*Essen, essen,*" they shouted, making hand gestures to their mouths. She pointed to the pantry, and they helped themselves to whatever they found there that they wanted. When they left, the pantry was empty. Thus began regular visits of Germans commandeering provisions for their troops.

"The Germans came to the mill last night," Ilija said on another morning when he arrived red-eyed and late for breakfast. "Johann and I heard their truck pull up, then banging on the window. I thought they'd break the glass."

"Isn't it unusual for them to come at night? I thought they were afraid of being ambushed," Mara said. The children stopped eating and listened. "How did they know you were there?"

"They must have heard the mill motor. You know how noisy it is. And the window—I'm sure the light is visible from the street'" Ilija replied. "When I unbolted the door, six soldiers pushed in, flashed their rifles, and demanded flour. I'm amazed at how much German I can understand." He sighed.

"They took most of the family flour. And the sacks waiting by the door for customers—they took those, too. I tried to steer them away. But it was no use." He grimaced. "When customers came this morning for their flour, I had to explain. It wasn't easy. I told them not to leave their flour overnight anymore."

Late one summer night a few months later, a voice came out of the darkness accompanied by banging on the door. *"Mi smo Partizani."* "We're Partisans; let us in!" The banging and shouting woke the family. Ilija rolled out of bed and unlocked the door. Mara wrapped a shawl around her and followed behind him.

Six armed men dressed in rag-tag bits of various uniforms marched in. None of their faces looked familiar, but the five-pointed star on their caps identified them as Partisans. The noise had awakened the children, and they stood to the side watching. "We're hungry," the men said, focusing their eyes on Mara.

Mara quickly started a fire in the wood stove from kindling kept in a pail beside it. She found leftover smoked goose meat, some cheese, and a loaf of bread in the pantry; she quickly began warming the meat. Sitting at the kitchen table, the strangers leaned their rifles and automatic weapons against their chairs within easy reach. As they waited, one of them checked his watch. Another got up and peered cautiously out the window. They seemed wary of running into Nazis or the other resistance group. Though both resistance groups were fighting to free the land from the Germans, as time went on, they had begun to fight each other for control of the country after the war.

Ilija brought out the customary *šljivovica* plum brandy while the men waited for their meal. Afterward, Mara handed them a sack. "Take this food with you," she said. "There's meat, cheese, and bread."

On other nights, members of the Chetniks resistance group showed up, ammunition belts worn across their chests and peaked caps or sheepskin hats bearing the crown symbol on their heads. Both resistance groups hid during the day to avoid capture by the Nazis. Many of the Chetniks wore familiar faces. They were friends from adjacent villages.

"Bake us some *gibanica*," they directed when they visited. While Mara prepared the cheese strudel, Ilija again brought out the *šljivovica*. It was the all-occasion hospitality drink, never offered to the Nazis. When the Chetniks left, it was with satisfied stomachs, a song on their lips, and arms laden with food.

Another afternoon German trucks came again while Ilija worked in the yard. Always they chose the large houses, where they expected to find plenty of food.

One early morning when Mara came into the mill, she found Ilija scooping flour out of the family bin and pouring it into a hemp sack. "What are you doing, Ilija?" she asked.

"We can't leave all our flour here anymore. It's not safe," he said. He filled the sack and tied it securely. "We'll have to start burying our flour and our food. I don't mind feeding our own, those who protect us, but when it comes to our occupiers, that's another story. If they keep coming back, we'll soon run out."

That night Ilija dug a hole in Mara's little garden near the house while Mara watched. He had filled a large wooden vat with flour and covered it tightly with canvas tied round with rope. Dropping the vat into the hole, he covered it with dirt, and rolled a large rock over the spot. Then he dug another hole nearby, threw in some clean straw, and filled it with potatoes, carrots, and several heads of cabbage just harvested, covering everything with dirt and patting it down. "There, that should do it," he said, wiping his forehead with the back of his hand.

And so began the hiding of their produce as well as their valuables. In times such as these, everything was subject to confiscation. "I have these two beautiful *libada* jackets," Mara remarked to Ilija one day. "I've been saving them for my future daughters-in-law. No one makes these anymore. I should hide them somewhere." She took the hand-made folk jackets of burgundy velvet with long wide sleeves, trimmed along the edges and back with gold braid in a Turkish design, and folded them into a tin box lined with wool. Then she added some gold coins and other valuables. Ilija dug a hole in the yard and buried the box.

"We seem to be living our lives on two levels these days, one in the open and one underground," Mara commented to Ilija one night as they dug up some of their produce. "It's a wonder we remember where everything is buried."

Everyone now began hiding provisions so they would have enough for themselves and their families. Farmers still brought their grain to the mill for processing but waited while it was being ground or picked it up before nightfall. Present circumstances required them to take all precautions.

Strangers who showed up at their door Mara honored as guests, recalling the biblical story of Abraham who showed hospitality to three travelers. Though Abraham's strangers turned out to be angels, there was no chance any of these visitors would fall into that category. Nevertheless, Serb custom dictated hospitality to all.

"It's gotten so that anybody can be pounding on our door day or night," someone in the family remarked. "Germans flushing out Partisans and Chetniks. Partisans tracking down Chetniks. Chetniks searching for Partisans. Meanwhile, across the Sava River in the Croatian state, just seven miles from their home, Ustash extremists pursued and executed both Chetniks and Partisans.

"Everything is becoming scarce," Milorad said to Mara and Ilija one day after returning from a trip to buy provisions. "The Nazis commandeer leather from the factories for their own needs, so leather goods have become unavailable for the people. Some of our neighbors are wearing wooden-soled shoes."

"Fortunately, we have animals," Ilija replied. "They give us meat to eat and leather for our shoes." Ilija had dried some hides that he had cured—calf hide for the top of the shoes and steer hide for the rest.

"This should be enough for two pairs," he said, cutting large pieces from the hides. The shoemaker can make a pair for me and keep the rest as payment. My shoes are wearing out."

Village life still moved in harmony with the seasons. On the outside, people clung to familiar daily routines, trying to preserve some semblance of normality despite the war. On the inside, they were being changed, imperceptibly, unconsciously. As the war dragged on, senses became heightened, emotions repressed, thinking and behavior altered. Mara's belief system and staunch faith helped insulate her from the evils of wartime and inspired her to look for the good.

"How long do you think this war will last?" asked a customer waiting at the mill for his flour. Customers often passed the time speculating about the war. During the summer months, the twins helped their father and listened to the talk.

"This guy Hitler seems invincible. His armies have won every battle," another responded.

"Mark my words. A defeat is coming. His armies aren't doing too good in Russia," commented a third man. "Hitler expected his troops to return as conquerors before the first winter. They've been there three winters now."

"Leave it to the Russian winter—faithful like a true ally," his companion declared. "It finished Napoleon. Let's hope Hitler fares no better."

21
Miracle at Midday

Ilija burst into the kitchen open-mouthed, just as Mara set a platter of apple fritters on the table. Their fragrance seemed to escape his notice. "You're just in time for breakfast, Ilija. We're ready to eat." She joined the children, who sat at the table with eager, hungry faces.

Ilija closed his mouth, removed his black felt hat, and stood at the head of the table. Everyone rose as he recited the Lord's Prayer, then sat and dived into their meal. In the chatter that followed, Mara noticed that Ilija seemed strangely distracted. Furtive glances darted from under his brows, and he played nervously with his fork, hardly touching his food. Finally, he pushed away from the table and spoke.

"Mara! Children! Johann stopped here before I came in. He had just come from Šabac." All eyes lifted toward Ilija. News from Johann these days carried weight. "Johann said he overheard some German officers discussing the ambush that occurred last week just down the road. You remember. A group of Partisans killed two German soldiers near our neighbor's cornfield." He paused and drew a large breath.

"Johann said the Germans plan to punish the town." His gaze circled the table. "They're sending a retribution expedition of *panzers* [tanks]. They should be on their way from Šabac right now."

Mara and the others sat stunned. "They're going to punish innocent villagers?" Mara finally managed to ask indignantly. "We had nothing to do with it."

"That doesn't matter to them. Their rule is a hundred lives for each German soldier lost."

Suddenly, the flimsy illusion of a loving family eating a normal breakfast vanished like morning mist in the heat of the sun. Breakfast was over. It was all a charade. They were at war, and nothing was normal anymore.

"I alerted my brothers," Ilija continued, "and Johann passed the word to the neighbors. By now, they're probably all in the woods. We must save our lives and hide until the tanks are gone, never mind what happens to the house." He stood up and started to go.

But Mara did not budge, nor did the children. When Ilija glanced back, he saw her sitting at the table, head bowed, eyes shut, the children looking to her for direction.

Is this the time, O Lord? Will You honor my faith? Is it Your will? Would it be foolhardy? Mara's mind seethed with questions. She longed for her family and neighbors to know God on a personal basis, to trust Him as their Friend, to experience His love as she had. Her many prayers had ascended seeking an opportunity for God to demonstrate His power and love, and now she struggled. Sitting there, praying for wisdom, Mara made a decision.

Looking up, her eyes met Ilija's. "Ilija, I'm staying here." Her voice sounded calm. "I believe God will save our house. I really do. None of us is guilty for the deaths of those boys. God will honor my faith, I feel sure. Please understand."

Ilija's face blanched. "You can't mean that, Mara! It's crazy to stay here. The tanks are on their way even now! We must go! Forget the house. We can build another. Save your life! Save the children!" His voice sounded frantic, desperate. "Children, come with me!" he urged. Again he started toward the door.

But the children remained beside their mother, exchanging glances, staying put. The reality of tanks heading toward them on a mission of destruction apparently escaped their understanding. The danger of being killed never seemed to be real. The children's faith lay in their mother. Her faith was anchored in God.

"You could stay with us, Ilija." Mara's voice followed him from her seat. He stopped at the door, his hand on the knob. "I can't stay, Mara. I don't have your faith. My unbelieving presence would only sabotage your prayers." He turned, agonizingly from the door. "Please, Mara, come. I beg you. Children, how can I let you stay?"

Mara heard the grief and fear in his voice, but she remained steadfast. The children did not move, except to turn their heads from one parent to the other and to each other. Ilija was big and strong enough to physically drag them out, Mara knew. He must have some semblance of faith to let them stay.

Seeing no response, a dejected Ilija walked out the door. It clicked softly behind him. In the quiet room Mara and the children exchanged glances. Fragments of food lay drying on plates in disarray on the table; the platter was empty now; the aroma of fritters stale. They strained their ears to hear. Somewhere in the distance outside, a low rumble, like something menacing that swelled from deep beneath the ground, was growing louder.

"Children, we must close the windows." Mara said, quickly standing up. She walked to one of the casement windows facing the street. Nata and Vera ran to another, the twins to a third. Pulling the outside casements closed and fastening them shut, they closed and locked the inside casements, then folded the paneled wooden spaletine shutters over them, blocking all light from the outside. In the darkened room, the only light filtering in came through the glass panels on the entrance doors facing the courtyard in the back and from a small window in the hallway.

Having secured all six windows facing the street, Mara and the children returned to the kitchen table, where Mara picked up her Bible and began to read its promises out loud in the dim light. Huddling close, the children listened. " 'The Lord is my light and my salvation; whom shall I fear? the Lord is the strength of my life; of whom shall I be afraid? . . . . Though an host should encamp against me, my heart shall not fear: though war should rise against me, in this will I be confident. . . . For in the time of trouble he shall hide me in His pavilion' [Psalm 27:1–5]. 'Fear thou not; for I am with thee: be not dismayed; for I am thy God:

I will strengthen thee; yea, I will help thee; yea I will uphold thee with the right hand of my righteousness. Behold, all they that were incensed against thee shall be ashamed and confounded; . . . . them that contended with thee: they that war against thee shall be as nothing . . . For I the Lord thy God will hold thy right hand" (Isaiah 41:10–13).

Mara closed her Bible, placed it on the table, and dropped to her knees. On the woolen rug she had woven, Nata, Vera, Cveja, and Voja formed a kneeling circle around her. She raised her head, held her clasped hands high, eyes tightly shut, and began to pray: "Almighty Father and God, hear our prayer. My children and I come before You seeking divine protection. Enemy tanks are on their way to destroy us, our homes, our little village, our world. But You, Lord, delight to save. You overrule evil. Almighty God, there is none like You. Of whom shall we be afraid? Glorify Your name, Lord, I pray, so that those who witness Your power may truly believe.

"Protect us now, I ask You, not because we are worthy, but for the sake of Your name, that You may be known and honored. As You delivered those who trusted in You in all ages, deliver us now, we plead." Then she ran through the Bible, starting with baby Moses, proceeding to Joseph in prison, Daniel in the lions' den, and his companions in the fiery furnace, reciting their deliverance.

Outside, the rumble grew louder, like the thunder of an approaching storm. Clattering treads scraped the gravel road. Diesel engines roared, unmuffled, to amplify the sound and strike terror in the heart. Yet, Mara was unafraid. Her children trusted her. She had courage enough for all of them. She continued to pray: "Oh, Father, am I doing the right thing? You see me here with these children that You gave me. Please protect them. Glorify Your name that others may believe. Protect us with Your mighty hand."

When Mara tired of kneeling, she sat. Bent over, head touching her knees, arms extended in front of her, she prayed still. The twins and their sisters reclined in various positions as they tired. When Mara stopped praying, Nata began. When Nata stopped, Vera took up the prayer. Cveja and Voja took turns.

Soon, the terrible racket closed in and drowned out their voices so that they could not hear themselves above the din. The thick brick walls of the house began to vibrate. Doors rattled on their hinges. Window sashes and shutters chattered to a nervous rhythm.

When the noise level indicated the arrival of the first tank, Mara pulled her children down and lay beside them. They pressed their bodies as flat to the floor as they could, faces down, arms drawn close, hands clasped over their ears to drown out the deafening noise. For a moment, she shuddered. A tank passed by outside. The noise was terrible. Then a calm surrounded her as she remembered the Bible promises.

But soon the vibrations began to diminish, the intense noise slackened. Mara opened her eyes and sat up. "The tank passed and didn't shoot!" Nata shouted, jumping up, her eyes full of wonder. The children cheered.

"It had to pass Uncle Milosav's and Mihajlo's house first," Vera shouted, "but it didn't fire—not once!" The realization made them laugh and cry and thank God, all at the same time.

But soon the rumble and clatter began building again. The house shook. The windows and doors shuddered. Again, Mara and her children dropped to the floor and lay prostrate, praying. The noise of the tank again eclipsed their voices, yet Mara knew God's ears heard every word.

Once more the vibrations subsided. Still no shelling. They sat up and shouted. No rumbling tanks or growls of war could hush their glad voices and praise.

". . . two, three," Voja and Cveja had started counting. *How many more tanks will there be?* Mara wondered. By the time the third tank passed, Mara and the children were shouting praises to God at the top of their lungs. Then, just as they heard the fourth tank approach, a tremendous double burst of shellfire exploded in the direction in which the tanks were proceeding. The explosion jolted them and shook the house to its foundation. They fell silent, wondering, not daring to go to the window. "The tank must have fired somewhere beyond our house," Mara concluded.

Another tremendous double explosion shook the house, then another, as tanks continued to pass, firing from what seemed the same location. "We once saw a *panzer* shoot at a thick brick wall," Cveja recalled. "The first shell hit the wall and made a hole; the second shell went through the hole and burst into a ball of fire."

"One of the houses on our street might have been hit," Nata suggested. Mara felt Vera roll over beside her and grasp her arm.

One by one, the tanks approached and passed their house, the noise ebbing and flowing as each tank came and went. Each time, shelling exploded in the distance. Finally, the shelling stopped, the tremors ceased, the noise died away.

"We counted sixteen tanks," Cveja reported.

"They're gone now!" the children chorused, jumping up. Nata arose and looked at her mother, who sat on the floor, rubbing a muscle in her leg. A few minutes later, the racket resumed and began to intensify.

"They're coming back!" Vera screamed in horror.

"Oh, Lord, please don't let them shell us this time," Mara prayed, dropping to the floor once more.

Again, the house shook; the window sashes shuddered. Again, they fell prostrate on the floor and prayed. The noise ebbed and flowed as before. "They're moving faster this time," Voja shouted over the din.

"And there's no shelling!" Cveja added. In chorus now, the children counted sixteen tanks again. Then they waited. The long, menacing flow of steel and fire faded into a low rumble, like a thunder storm moving away. It was over.

In the eerie silence that followed, waves of overwhelming joy and relief flowed over the little group. Mara and the girls bubbled out their gratitude to God for His miraculous deliverance. Mara pulled herself up slowly, feeling cramped from kneeling in one position for so long. Nata rose and stretched. "We've been praying for almost two hours," Mara observed, checking her watch.

"Let's see what happened," she said, going to the window. She unlocked and pulled open the spaletin shutters, then unlocked and opened the inside and outside casement windows. *What was that shelling about?* The thought nagged in her mind.

Suddenly she drew back. In the clear, blue sky outside, ugly black smoke drifted toward them.

"Let's go outside," Nata suggested, turning toward the door at the back of the house. Vera scampered behind the twins who slipped ahead and down the four steps. "Wait, children," Mara cautioned as they rounded the side of the building. A fence blocked their view of the road, but the sky above them had turned an angry black. The rank odor of smoke mingling with noxious diesel fumes and sulfur stung their nostrils and burned their eyes. Mara opened the gate. The children spilled out.

Across the road, green fields of clover tinged red with blossoms spread out as before. To their right, in the direction of town, their pink-stuccoed grain mill with its red tile roof still stood beside the house. Next to it, the gray-stuccoed houses of Mihajlo and Milorad with their red tile roofs remained intact. The brick factory still stood, set back on the other side of the road.

And then they looked to their left. Milorad's house next to theirs as well as the next four houses were untouched and unscathed. But after that point lay a scene of devastation. As far as their horrified eyes could see, on both sides of the road farther away, smoke billowed from charred hulks of homes. Flames leaped and crackled. Some of the roofs had collapsed, and only solid brick chimneys rose as scarred survivors of the fire storm.

"Oh!" Mara exclaimed, covering her mouth to quell a scream. Their neighbors' homes, their once-lovely village, their little world, lay in ashes. Sadness overwhelmed the joy she had felt just moments before.

Soon people drifted out of the woods—in twos and little groups—small children running ahead. Some carried blankets, a jug of water, a half-empty sack of food they had taken with them. At the sight of the burning shells that were once their homes, women wailed aloud, beating their breasts with their fists and crying.

Ilija was the first to reach his family. "Mara, children, are you all right? I can't believe what I see!" His voice was full of wonder, questions, and distress. All eight Vitorovich houses stood intact, along with four of their closest neighbors' homes, stretching half a mile along the main road.

Milorad and Mihajlo and their wives ran toward them. Everyone spoke at the same time, repeating the same questions, uttering the same exclamations. And then Johann appeared.

"Look, Johann. See what happened!" Someone wailed to him as he approached, pointing to the rubble, as if he might have deterred his German countrymen from their malevolent mission. Johann looked on with sadness in his eyes, but he directed his feet toward Mara.

"Where were you when the tanks came, Mara?" he asked. "Did you go to the woods?"

The clamor of voices hushed. All eyes turned to Mara. Her face glowed, and her eyes brightened with gratitude. "Johann, the children and I were in the house. We stayed to pray."

Exclamations erupted from those who did not know. "She was in the house?" someone questioned incredulously.

Johann slapped his forehead with his palm. "Mara, Mara," he repeated. "I should have known. It makes sense now." Then he turned to Ilija to explain. The small group pressed close.

"This morning after I warned you about the tanks, I went home. All the way there, I felt terribly upset and depressed, wishing I could do something. Then an idea took hold of me. The farther I walked, the stronger the thought pressed on my mind. I couldn't push it away. As soon as I reached home, I took my shovel from the barn, slung it over my shoulder, and hurried back to Glušci." All eyes focused on Johann as he talked.

"The street was deserted when I got here. I guess everyone had gone to the woods. So I dug up the town sign and relocated it beyond the Vitorovich houses. I obviously couldn't stop the tanks; I couldn't save the entire town, but I hoped to save at least part of it."

A hush fell over the group. Loving arms reached out to embrace him. Johann turned again to Mara. "At the time, I never thought what would happen if they caught me. All I knew was this strange compulsion." He paused, a smile gladdening his face as he looked at Mara. "Now I understand why."

Crying neighbors ambled toward them, eyes wide with wonder and despair. "Your houses aren't damaged. There's not much left of ours."

"I'm so sorry," Mara said, reaching out, her heart heavy. How could she rejoice when so many others had suffered such loss?

"Mara was in her house praying," Johann explained. Then he told them about the strange compulsion and what he did. "I shudder to think what would have happened had I not done that. God was looking out for you, Mara. I wish I could have done more."

"It's not your fault, Johann," someone said. "They were out to punish the town. Our houses would have been destroyed no matter what."

"Let us help you," Mara offered. "Where will you sleep? What will you do for food? We can give you some blankets."

"We still have our stables and cow sheds and our barns. They're untouched," one of the neighbors replied. "The weather's still warm. We can sleep in those. Our animals and crops have survived, but we have no place to stay or cook."

"Let us help you," Ilija said. "Come here tomorrow and eat with us."

"I'll make extra bread. Lila and Petra will help. We'll share," Mara offered.

For several weeks the villagers worked together, helped each other. Some began making their own unbaked bricks and started rebuilding. The people were used to adversity and hardship and had learned to survive. Every war had required them to rebuild, to reestablish their state.

As for Mara's miracle at midday, it remained an inspiration for a long time.

22
War Ends and a New Order Begins

"Look, Ilija!" Mara called out, pointing upward. "Planes!" Ilija was nailing loose boards in the fence when Mara came out. He heard them, too, a low droning sound like distant prolonged thunder. Standing up, hammer in hand, he shielded his eyes and gazed at the sky.

"They look like a swarm of locusts," Mara observed. "Have you ever seen so many?"

"Germans don't fly that high. They don't have to," Ilija said, thoughtfully. "It's Americans! American planes, our Allies!" his voice escalated in pitch.

Others noticed, too, and drew the same conclusion, for loud cheering and applause rang out from several directions. "Maybe now this war will end," Mara sighed.

For the last few weeks there had been no newspaper or radio communications, but in the summer of 1944, the grapevine sizzled with the news, "The war has turned."

Indeed, the war had begun to turn in the Allies' favor. Just the year before, Mussolini had been arrested, and Italy capitulated. The Allies' recent landing at Normandy won a decisive battle for Europe. And in Russia, at Stalingrad, dozens of German generals and hundreds of thousands of starving, freezing German troops had surrendered.

"The Germans rode in as conquerors; now they're leaving on foot and in defeat," more than one report observed. From all along the fifteen-hundred-mile-long eastern front, German troops were retreating, the Red Army in hot pursuit.

When Cveja and Voja came home from school in June for summer break, they bore horrifying tales of events they had witnessed in Šabac. "We saw people hanging from lampposts on our street. Every time we went to school, we passed them hanging there. Jewish friends and shop owners disappeared. All the Romas disappeared from their section of town. We watched German prisoners dig up a mass grave. Now we know what happened to the 120 men from Uzveće who disappeared."

Hearing these tales from her sons, Mara shuddered. "Children's eyes should not see such horrible things, such tragedy. So many innocent victims," she said. She shook her head in grief. Witnesses of violence and injustice were victims, too.

"The Germans are coming. Scores of thousands of them are retreating from Russia toward Germany. Some have already reached this region," Johann reported to Ilija one early September morning when he found him and his boys sweeping the platforms at the mill, while geese and chickens wandered around, pecking at the ground, picking up the fallen grains. "Many have walked most of the way. They're starving and desperate. Whatever food and horses they find they'll take."

"There's not much left. The Partisans and Nazis have already seized all our carriages, coaches, and horses," Ilija replied. "One horse and wagon is all we have left. Without them, we can't haul anything or work the land. Thanks, Johann, for the warning."

As soon as Johann left, Ilija gave Voja instructions. "Ask your mother for a sack lunch, then take the horse and wagon and hide them in the woods." He turned to Cveja. "Cveja, go tell Milorad about this."

A few minutes later, Milorad's eldest son, now thirty-five-years-old, drove up with his family's last horse and wagon, and the two cousins rode into the nearby woods to hide, hoping the enemy would sweep through before nightfall.

The bright sun rose high in the sky and then dropped toward the horizon. Still the two cousins did not return from the woods. Mara looked toward the road throughout the day, hoping to see some sign of their return, praying as she worked. At evening, she left the outside door unlocked so Voja could come in. Then she knelt in her room. It was pitch black when she heard the door open and footsteps in the hallway.

"Voja?" she called out hopefully, running to meet him. "You stayed so long. Are you all right?" At the sound of conversation, Cveja, Nata, and Vera rushed in from their rooms. None of them could sleep while their brother's whereabouts remained unknown.

When Voja dropped into a chair, his siblings quickly surrounded the table, anxious to hear of his experience. "We were deep in the woods, hiding in a small clearing. With trees all around, we thought nobody could see us," he began. "Suddenly, we heard a shrill voice scream, 'Halt!' It just about scared me out of my skin. Before we knew it, two German officers stood there, pointing guns at us. One had binoculars hanging from around his neck. I guess that's how they spotted us."

Cveja leaned toward his brother. His sisters listened breathless.

"The big one, the colonel, ordered the other officer to shoot us. It was the first time I had heard German spoken outside of class, but I understood it. Mother, they were going to kill us! I had to do something." He swallowed hard. "I slipped under the machine gun the other soldier held on us and ran to the big officer, asking him in German, 'Why do you want to kill us?' He looked so surprised. I think he liked it that I spoke German because he smiled a little. I told him, 'We're not Communists. Take our horses and wagons, but please don't kill us.' He thought a minute and changed his mind. He told the other officer to get into the wagons. We rode with them through the woods. We weren't sure what they'd do with us. Then when we came to the road and saw the German troops, they let us go."

The girls fell back in their seats. "Thank You, God," Mara exclaimed.

"I knew you were praying for us, Mother," Voja turned to his mother. "That made me strong." He paused. "You know what? I think speaking German saved my life. I'm glad you encouraged us to study it."

When September rolled around, school did not open. All classes were suspended for the year. Everything in the country was in disorder and confusion. Events were occurring in rapid-fire succession.

As Tito's Communist Partisans liberated one area of the country after another, they set up their own interim administration. By now Draža

Mihajlovich's Chetniks were out of the picture. Because of Nazi reprisals on innocent civilians when German soldiers were killed, the Chetniks had diverted their energies to sabotage missions and passing intelligence to the Allies for a later mission. But the Partisans' aggressive assaults against Nazi troops had drawn the support of the Allies.

By October, the Partisans had driven the Germans out of a devastated Belgrade. People thronged the streets to welcome and cheer their liberators. They climbed onto the tanks, shouting "Long live Tito!" Some in the jubilant crowd played violins while others danced in the streets. Still others bombarded the victors with flowers.

In April 1945 Mussolini was dead, and Hitler committed suicide in his bunker. In May, a ruined Berlin fell, and the Germans surrendered unconditionally. The war was over, but everything everywhere was in flux.

Some time later, a man appeared at Mara's door. "Don't you know me, Mara?" he asked.

The face before her looked unfamiliar.

"I'm Živan. I was just released from prison, and I'm on my way home to Leka." During his four years in a prisoner of war camp in Germany, his hair had turned completely white.

"Oh, Živan, thank God you're alive," she said. Mara hugged him and invited him in to rest and eat.

With the end of hostilities, a strange silence fell upon the gaping wounds of a devastated world. Machine guns no longer hammered. Explosions did not rip the air. No planes droned through the night. In the war's chaotic conclusion, millions of homeless refugees wound up in camps for displaced persons. Many had suffered at the hands of their own people and feared to return to their own countries, some of which were now under Communist control.

Hiding among the countless victims were also Nazi collaborators and war criminals from every country of Europe. All had faced the same choices: how to respond to threats and hostilities and hateful dogmas. Some had turned traitor; some committed atrocities. Now, armed with new names and false identification papers, many of these escaped to other countries masquerading as innocents.

"Most of our cities lie in ruins. An entire generation has been deci-
mated. Many have lost their homes, and severe famine threatens in
many areas," a news reporter in Yugoslavia recounted. Fortunately, the
fertile soil in the Glušci region provided sustenance.

"Marshall Tito and his Communist Partisans have wasted no time re-
structuring the country," another newscast summarized. "The new regime
has set itself up in the former king's royal chambers in Belgrade. It has de-
veloped a new constitution and new laws and formed a one-party central-
ized state." In this system, political freedom and civil rights were restricted.
Partisans who had fought gained leadership positions and recognition.

"Where's Johann?" Ilija asked one morning. "He hasn't been to work
for two days. It's not like him." Upon further inquiry, he learned that
the government had rounded up all those accused, or suspected, of collaborating with the Nazis. Johann, being German, was among the sus-
pects arrested and taken to Šabac.

Ilija immediately set off for Šabac. When he returned later that day,
he reported on his trip to Mara and the family, concerned for Johann's
welfare. "I saw the Communist commander of the detention camp,"
Ilija told them. "He's not a local man. He knew nothing about Johann.
I told him that Johann has worked for us the past twenty years and that
he definitely was not a collaborator. I told him that Johann had helped
the townspeople many times, warning us of danger. The man promised
to look into Johann's file and told me to come back tomorrow."

The next day Ilija returned to Šabac. Again, when he came home he
reported what had happened. "Johann's file is clear," he said. "The commander found no accusations against him. But he needs proof in order
to release him. A signed petition with six hundred names will do."

Ilija and his brothers immediately drafted a petition, and early the
next day they went from house to house in Glušci and Uzveće, seeking
signatures. "We have twelve hundred signatures," Milorad counted at
the end of the day. "More than double the number required." The next
morning, the three men delivered the petition to the commander.

"He was shocked that we got back to him so fast," Ilija told Mara
upon his return. "The commander said they would verify the names and

signatures against the village roster. If everything is in order, Johann will be released in a couple of weeks."

Three days later, Johann showed up at their door. "Johann, you're back!" What a joy it was for the family as well as the other villagers who celebrated his release!

In June 1945, the government announced: "For those who want to make up the past school year, we will offer a three-month intensive school curriculum. Classes will meet six days a week from 8:00 A.M. to 5:00 P.M. Russian language study will be added to the mandatory foreign language curriculum.

"We need to go," Cveja said to Voja when he heard the announcement. Cveja and Voja returned to Šabac and registered for their fifth year of high school.

"Children, I've brought you a soccer ball," Mara said on one of her subsequent visits to Šabac. She offered the ball to her twins. "Živan made it from scraps of leather and stuffed it with Leka's old woolen stockings. I hope you can use it. Supplies are still short."

In September, after the twins completed the crash curriculum, they returned home for a one-week break before starting their next school year. In their absence from home, things had drastically changed.

"The government left us seventy-five acres for the entire family—twenty-five for each brother and his sons," Ilija explained. "The other 175 acres it confiscated without any compensation. It's part of the agrarian reform. The government is distributing the land to those who have little or none."

"But if people have never farmed, they won't now how to work the land," Cveja pointed out.

"That's just it. Some don't even own an ox or a horse," Ilija replied.

Gradually, for some, the land given them fell into disuse. "Our businesses have been nationalized. The state owns them now," Mara told her sons. "It's very difficult for our men. They've worked so hard to build them up. Now strangers are in charge. It's humiliating for them to be treated as hired hands."

When September arrived and it was time to return to school, Voja balked. "I don't want to go back, Cveja," he told his brother.

"But we have only three more years to graduate. It's a mistake not to finish."

"Father needs help, and I'm the elder son. A smaller piece of land needs more efficiency. I can help him."

Here, again, their sister Nata came to the fore. "Please, Father, don't let Voja stay home from school," she urged.

"And who will plow the land? How will I harvest it?" Ilija asked.

"I'll do the work. Your sons need a good education. At least they can get that from this regime. We don't have our industries anymore. How will they support a family when they grow up?"

"I'll help, too," scrawny Vera chimed in. She was now eighteen years old.

The district pastor and his wife contributed to the debate. Their daughter, two years younger than the twins, had grown up with the boys. Her parents had hoped that one day she and Cveja would marry. If Voja dropped out, Cveja might also.

"OK, OK, I'll go," Voja finally conceded. "Father says I should." Cveja and Voja returned to school together for their sixth year of high school. *Baka* had grown old and feeble, so they moved to another church member's house.

In November 1945, newscasts reported, "A constituent assembly has declared Yugoslavia a republic. King Peter has been condemned. Draža Mihajlovich, a former colonel in the Yugoslav royal army and the leader of the Chetniks, has been accused of collaborating with the Nazis."

Tito was now in full control of the country. Mihajlovich vehemently denied the accusation and was supported by the five hundred American pilots who had been shot down over occupied Serbia and saved by Mihajlovich's men. Nevertheless, he was executed, along with numerous others who were Tito's rivals.

While the twins were in school that year, Vera decided to take an apprenticeship in Šabac on a knitting machine. The twins' landlady put another bed in their room, and Vera stayed six months. When she returned home, her skills and newly purchased knitting machine provided a way to earn money.

23
A New Idea Versus an Old

Clack! Clack! Clack! Clack! Clack! The distant racket grew steadily louder. Inside the house, Mara stopped and listened. Some strange vehicle seemed to be coming down the road and approaching the house. "What in the world?" she muttered to herself. Wiping her hands on her embroidered linen apron, she opened the door and stepped outside to look around.

Through the open gate, a huge, Russian-built farm tractor, pulling a four-bladed plow, was turning into the property. Following it with curious eyes, Mara watched it rumble past her and park in back under her favorite apple tree that had just begun to turn green. A startled hen, which had been pecking and scratching the ground beneath the tree, scattered with her brood in a flurry of clucks and peeps.

More rumbling and clacking sounded out in the road. Mara's head swung toward the open gate, where a second huge tractor was turning in. As it passed the house, a third tractor appeared in the open gate. Then a few yards behind it, still another followed. Soon four huge tractors, each pulling a plow, stood helter-skelter beneath the trees at the back of the house.

"Ilija, what's going on?" she called out, spying him and Milorad talking over the fence that divided their properties. Ilija raised his brows and shrugged his shoulders. Voja and Cveja stood near them, taking in the scene. On this balmy Friday afternoon in the spring of 1946, all five watched the proceedings like observers in a theater—interested and wondering, "What happens next?"

Just then a dark green Mercedes whirred through the gate, horn honking, diesel engine clattering. It drove past the onlookers, made a U-turn, and screeched to a stop near the four tractors. Cars were a rare sight in the village, and a Mercedes even rarer, but Mara recognized this one immediately as the vehicle driven by Draga, their neighbor, with whose family Mara had been long-time friends.

Stepping out of the car, the tall man in his thirties, wearing a military officer's cap, tossed a relaxed salute to the four young drivers, each now standing beside his tractor. Then he turned toward Mara, who was descending the stairs and walking toward him. "Greetings, *Tetka* Mara," he said, smiling.

"Draga, my son, why are these tractors here?" she asked as she stood before him, her kerchief-framed round face turned upward and her eyes full of questions.

The two tall, strong men watching by the fence in silence raised an eyebrow and threw each other a knowing look. Draga, a decorated Partisan Communist who had fought the Nazis for four years and now served as president of the village *kolhoz,* or collective farm, was not accustomed to being questioned.

"Well, *Tetka* Mara," he replied respectfully, clearing his throat, "tomorrow morning we plan to plow the land behind your house. We just want to leave the tractors here overnight."

Mara's bushy eyebrows lowered like storm clouds over a clear blue sky. *Tomorrow? Tomorrow is Sabbath,* she thought to herself.

"Draga, this land has been in our family for four generations. Surely, you know that," she responded. "Since we didn't sell it to the government, in God's eyes the land still belongs to us. It's still our family's land."

Draga's smile faded from his face. The directness of Mara's statement caught him off guard, and he shifted to one foot.

"Tomorrow is the seventh day, God's holy day of rest," Mara continued. "God forbids us to work on that day. I'm asking you not to plow this land on the Sabbath. Can't the work wait until Monday?"

Draga tilted his cap forward to scratch the back of his dark-haired head. *"Tetka* Mara," he finally said with a sheepish grin, "this belief of yours in

God—well, that's an old idea!" He chuckled, gestured widely with his hands. "The new idea is that there is no God." His hands fell to his sides.

"Oh, no, my son." Mara shook her head. "It's just the opposite. Seeking after God is a new idea," Mara countered quickly. "That there is no God is a very old notion. As long as three thousand years ago there were people who thought like that. The Bible gives them a certain name."

Draga thinned his lips and cast a glimpse over his shoulder at the young drivers. He was their hero. His reputation was on the line. They watched and listened intently. He turned to Mara with a puzzled look. "A name, you say? What kind of name?"

"Well, Draga, it's not the nicest one. I'll let you read it yourself."

"I don't . . ." he began, but before he could finish, Mara was climbing the steps to the house. She returned with a worn-looking black book with slips of paper peeking out from between its dog-eared pages.

"A king wrote these words," she continued, leafing through the pages, as if there had been no interruption. "His name was King David." In the presence of the Holy Book, Draga immediately removed his cap and put it under his arm. Evidently, he had not yet forgotten the reverence of the old ways. His companions waiting by the tractors did the same. "Here is what I was looking for. It's Psalm fourteen, verses one and two," Mara said and began to read. " 'The fool hath said in his heart, There is no God. . . . The Lord looked down from heaven upon the children of men, to see if there were any that did understand, and seek God.' Read it for yourself, Draga. Here." She extended the open Bible to Draga. His face turned crimson.

"I . . . I've never held a Bible before," he said, staring uncertainly at Mara and then at the Book. He reached out and took it carefully in his hands and read the verse where Mara's finger pointed: " 'The fool has said . . .' " his voice faded, but his lips continued to move. Returning the Book to Mara, he laughed a staccato, insecure laugh. Then he threw a glance over his shoulder at his men, shouting, "Say, fellows, this Book calls us fools!" They laughed too.

When he turned back to Mara, there was a somber look on his face. "That's fine, *Tetka* Mara, for you to honor your holy day. My father is also a religious man. He goes to church on Sunday. However, if bad weather threatens and he needs to harvest his crops that day, he asks the priest for exemption. Now, you're not going to tell me the Bible specifically forbids plowing on Saturday, are you?" He cocked his head to the side with an air of confidence.

"Draga, let me first read what God says about the Sabbath." She flipped through the pages to Exodus 20:8–11. " 'Remember the sabbath day, to keep it holy. Six days shalt thou labour, and do all thy work: But the seventh day is the sabbath of the Lord thy God: in it thou shalt not do any work, thou, nor thy son, nor thy daughter, thy manservant, nor thy maidservant, nor thy cattle, nor thy stranger that is within thy gates: For in six days the Lord made heaven and earth, the sea, and all that in them is, and rested the seventh day: wherefore the Lord blessed the sabbath day, and hallowed it.' "

Draga frowned. "So where am I in that picture?"

"You're the stranger within my gates," Mara replied. "Sunday is a man-made holy day, so men can give all the exemptions they want regarding Sunday. But God blessed the seventh day and made it sacred, and He forbids plowing on that day." She turned to read again from her book, this time from Exodus 34:21. " 'Six days you shall work, but on the seventh day you shall rest: in plowing time and in harvest you shall rest.' " (NKJV.)

Draga looked incredulous. He shook his head. This undefeated warrior had been defeated by a gentle little woman and a worn old book. "Let me see that." He bent toward Mara and squinted at the Book. When he read the words himself, his voice sounded earnest as he asked, "Tell me, *Tetka* Mara, what would happen to me if I disregarded everything you have read to me?" He stroked his chin thoughtfully.

"I don't know, Draga. That's God's business. But I can read you what He says." She turned the pages until she found Ezekiel 3:19 and read, " 'Yet if thou warn the wicked, and he turn not from his wickedness, nor from his wicked way, he shall die in his iniquity; but thou hast delivered thy soul.' "

She let him read the words himself, then closed the Bible. Draga drew back and glared at the Book in Mara's hands, his face pale. He spoke softly, as if to himself. "First this Book calls us fools, then it threatens us with death." For a long minute he remained silent. Then flashing a smile and placing his cap back on his head, he spun around and strode briskly toward his car, shouting to his men as he walked. "Drive those tractors to my backyard. Tomorrow we'll plow another field!"

Quickly the four men jumped onto their tractors and revved the engines. When Draga reached his car, he turned back for a last look at Mara. She was still standing where he had left her, still clasping her Bible in her hands. There was a bewildered expression on his face as he climbed into his car and started up the noisy motor. It was still there when he approached the men and Mara. "So long," he said, driving past and speeding through the gate and into the road.

One by one, the four tractors followed, clacking and rumbling slowly off the property, each driver acknowledging the observers with a nod of the head or a wave as he drove past. Through the hazy cloud of dust that swirled upward in their wake, enveloping the group like an unlikely blessing, they watched until the last tractor had turned and disappeared. As the cloud dispersed, they looked at each other. "Well, Mara, this is a good day!" Ilija said.

"A great day!" Milorad added. "You're priceless, Mara." Ilija and Milorad had come alive. Light sparkled in their eyes, and happy smiles gladdened their faces.

"Thank You, Jesus!" The praise rang out from Mara's lips.

"You know what? Victory is sweet," Ilija added. Mara wholeheartedly agreed. In a time when the struggle was no longer one to survive the war but to endure the peace, here was a small victory.

Milorad turned toward his house. Ilija put his arm around Mara's shoulder, and they walked to the house with Cveja and Voja following closely behind.

The wind stiffened and rustled the tops of the leafing trees. In the west, the sinking sun ushered in the Sabbath with a final burst of ruby rays, tinting and gilding the evening sky.

On Monday, Draga and the *kolhoz* tractors returned to plow the land. But never in all the years the family lived there did anyone come to work "their" land on Mara's Sabbath.

24
After the Last Goodbye

"It's almost time to say goodbye again," Mara said sadly one early September day as her sons prepared once again to return to school. It was 1948. In June the twins had graduated from the district high school in Šabac. They had just turned nineteen and had passed the university entrance exam; this time they were moving to Belgrade.

"I was wrong to want to keep you back from school," Ilija suddenly blurted out. "It scares me now to think I might have succeeded. What would you do? We have no businesses now, no land. You'd have no future."

"God was guiding all along," Mara replied. Then she turned to her boys. "We won't be able to help you with expenses," she apologized. "City living will cost more."

"Don't worry, Mother. We'll be fine," Cveja replied. "The most important thing is settled; we have a place to stay. We're really very lucky that Nata and Mića are willing to share their small apartment. From what we hear, apartments in Belgrade are very hard to find."

"At least the regime provides a free education," Voja added. "If we can find a part-time job while studying, we'll be OK. But we probably won't be able to afford too many visits home. Train fare is expensive."

Nata and Mića had married the year before and moved to Belgrade, where Mića started his own painting and decorating business. The regime had recently relaxed its restrictions and now allowed for small independent enterprises.

A few days later, the twins left. They moved in with their sister and her husband and enrolled in the College of Engineering at Belgrade University to pursue architectural studies. Each Sabbath, with Nata and newly baptized Mića, they attended the large Seventh-day Adventist church in Belgrade with almost a thousand members. "School is going well." Mara read Voja's first letter hungrily. "None of our classes fall on Sabbath this semester. We've been able to reschedule the labs scheduled for Sabbath. Most of our professors are not communists so they don't give us a hard time." Mara was ecstatic.

In a letter from her son written later that year, Mara read, "Two classes fall on Sabbath this semester. But our classmates fill us in on whatever we miss. You'll be happy to know that Cveja and I joined the church youth choir, and I'm playing my guitar in the mandolin orchestra." Mara lifted her face to heaven. *Thank You, Lord. The guitar idea worked! My heart is full.*

"Good news, Mother," another letter announced. "Cveja and I are preparing for baptism on June 28. Can you come?" Mara dropped the letter and fell to her knees. *Lord, You've answered all my prayers!*

And so on St. Vitus Day, Mara, Mića, and Nata watched as the twins in white robes, along with twenty-five other candidates, went down into the waters of the baptistery. The joy in Mara's heart overflowed. Sitting blissfully in the large sanctuary, amid the huge congregation, so unlike the small group meetings in the village homes that she was used to, Mara listened enthralled, watching her sons participate, praising God in her heart.

"All right, Mother," Voja asked later when they returned to the apartment, "which girl did you select for me? I saw you put on your glasses and inspect them during the service."

"You did? Well, son, I couldn't pick one," Mara replied, her face turning pink. "You must do that yourself. Just make sure she's a faithful Christian. And if she's pretty, like Rebecca and Rachel in the Bible, you'll love her more. I pray God will direct you in your choice."

"Mića's business is thriving, and we are getting fat on Nata's good cooking," another letter from her sons said. Unmentioned was the fact that Mića had begun to come home from work later each night and frequently absented himself from church. One day tragedy struck. Mića disappeared.

Months later, Nata showed up at the farm with her belongings in two suitcases.

"Nata! What are you doing here? What happened?" Mara asked when she saw her. Ilija happened to be there and took her bags.

"Mića is in prison. The authorities confiscated the apartment and evicted us. They even tried to take my furniture," she choked back the tears. "Fortunately, I saved the receipts. They were in my maiden name. You bought the furniture, Father, for my dowry. I stored my things in a friend's shed. With no job and no place to stay, I had to come home." She broke down and wept.

"This is always your home, my love," Mara said, comfortingly. "Tell us what happened from the beginning."

"Several months ago, two men came to the apartment looking for Mića. They were UDBA agents." She dried her eyes. "They flashed their badges. I told them Mića was still at work.

" 'We want him for questioning,' they said. For days they watched the house, but Mića didn't come home. He was nowhere to be found. Ten days later, we learned that the police had arrested him somewhere near the Italian border. They said he was trying to escape."

"But what did he do?" Ilija asked. "Why were they after him?"

"His name was on a membership list of some secret anti-Communist organization. The police somehow found it. Strange, I never suspected his involvement in politics. I should have known," Nata castigated herself. "The authorities sentenced him to ten years in prison. For months, we didn't know where he was. Ten years! Mother! What will I do?" She began crying again.

"How terrible for you, Nata! You'll be all right here," Mara comforted her.

"And what about the boys?" Ilija asked. "Where are they living now?"

"They found a room with one of the church members. They're OK." Nata replied, still sniffling.

In 1951 Vera and Duja married in a nearby village. Voja came from Belgrade to attend the wedding with the family. Since Ilija had suddenly taken ill and been hospitalized in Belgrade, Cveja stayed behind to be near his father. Everyone expected Ilija to recover and return home quickly, so Mara did not visit, knowing the twins would look after him.

About two weeks later, a visitor from city hall called on Mara. "Mrs. Vitorovich, I regret to inform you that we received a message from your sons in Belgrade," he said. "Your husband, Ilija, passed away this morning in the hospital." Mara was stunned and heartsick.

Family members made the trip to Belgrade for the funeral. When Mara inquired, the boys told her what happened. "We visited Father every day during his hospitalization. Then one day his bed was empty. When we asked the other patient in the room, he said Father had died that morning." At sixty-two years of age, Ilija was gone, and Mara was a widow again.

At the funeral service, the Belgrade church choir sang, and one of the pastors preached the service. The scripture for his sermon was 1 Thessalonians 4:13–18.

> But I would not have you to be ignorant, brethren, concerning them which are asleep, that ye sorrow not, even as others which have no hope. For if we believe that Jesus died and rose again, even so them also which sleep in Jesus will God bring with him. For this we say unto you by the word of the Lord, that we which are alive and remain unto the coming of the Lord shall not prevent them which are asleep. For the Lord himself shall descend from heaven with a shout, with the voice of the archangel, and with the trump of God: and the dead in Christ shall rise first. Then we which are alive and remain shall be caught up together with them in the clouds to meet the Lord in the air: and so shall we ever be with the Lord. Wherefore comfort one another with these words.

The resurrection! How my heart longs for that day, Mara thought to herself as she looked at her husband's lifeless form resting peacefully in the wooden casket.

After the funeral, the women in the family gathered around Mara in the kitchen, asking questions that had come up because of the sermon. "I'm confused about this, Mara," Petra said. "The souls of the dead are already in heaven, so what's the reason for the resurrection?" Mara took her Bible and prepared to answer.

"That's the point, Petra. We don't go to heaven when we die. There has to be a judgment first. The Bible teaches that the dead, good and bad, rest in the grave. Death is like a sleep. Except for Enoch and Elijah, whom God translated, and Moses, who was raised from the dead, nobody from earth is in heaven now." Mara found Acts 2:29, 34 and read. " 'Men and brethren, let me freely speak unto you of the patriarch David, that he is both dead and buried, and his sepulchre is with us unto this day. . . . For David is not ascended into the heavens.' You see, Paul says David is still in the grave. If he's still there, everybody else is also. That's why Jesus is coming back to earth, to take us home—because no one is there now."

"Why, that makes sense, Mara, but you know how we were taught— that the soul is immortal and goes to heaven," Lila said.

"Not according to the Bible," Mara replied. "When the Bible talks about souls, it means the whole person. The soul can be alive or dead. Let's go back to creation to see what it says." She picked up her Bible and read Genesis 2:7. " 'And the Lord God formed man of the dust of the ground, and breathed into his nostrils the breath of life; and man became a living soul.' See what it says? Man became a living soul when God breathed life into him. Before that, he was a dead soul. It doesn't say God put a soul in man's body."

She read further. " 'For as the body without the spirit is dead, so faith without works is dead also' [James 2:26]. 'Then shall the dust return to the earth as it was: and the spirit shall return unto God who gave it' [Ecclesiastes 12:7]. Spirit or breath—they mean the same. It's the breath that goes back to God when we die." Mara said.

"The Bible is clear. There is no such thing as an immortal soul. The Bible says, 'The soul that sinneth, it shall die' [Ezekiel 18:4]. So you see, the soul is mortal. When we die, we know nothing."

She turned the pages of her Bible again: " 'For the living know that they shall die: but the dead know not any thing, neither have they any more reward; for the memory of them is forgotten. Also their love, and their hatred, and their envy is now perished' [Ecclesiastes 9:5, 6]. 'So man lieth down, and riseth not: till the heavens be no more, they shall not awake, nor be raised out of their sleep. . . . His sons come to honour, and he knoweth it not; and they are brought low, but he perceiveth it not of them' [Job 14:12, 21].

"Do you see it?" Mara continued. "The idea of an immortal soul is based on the devil's lie. I'll read it to you. The serpent asked Eve if God had told her and Adam that they could not eat the fruit of every tree in the Garden. This is what Eve replied." Mara found Genesis 3:3. " 'But of the fruit of the tree which is in the midst of the garden, God hath said, Ye shall not eat of it, neither shall ye touch it, lest you die. And the serpent said unto the woman, Ye shall not surely die.' The devil lied. God said they would die if they disobeyed. The devil said they would not die. The teaching that we continue living after we die comes from Satan and paganism. Christians should know better," Mara said. "The problem is that people don't read the Bible for themselves. That's why they're confused. Never mind what others say. You need to know what God says."

Turning to the New Testament, Mara continued, "The Bible tells us that only God is immortal. Timothy says that God 'only hath immortality, dwelling in the light which no man can approach unto; whom no man hath seen, nor can see: to whom be honour and power everlasting. Amen' [1 Timothy 6:16]. He also says that Jesus 'hath abolished death, and hath brought life and immortality to light through the gospel' [2 Timothy 1:10].

"God promises immortality only to those who believe. You know the verse—John 3:16. It says, 'For God so loved the world, that he gave his only begotten Son, that whosoever believeth in him should not perish, but have everlasting life.' Unbelievers never have it. In the end, the wicked will perish and be no more. Listen to this," Mara continued, turning to other texts. "This one says that God 'will render to every man according to his deeds: To them who by patient continuance in well doing seek for glory and honour and immortality, eternal life' [Romans 2:5, 6, 7].

"And Paul says, 'Behold, I shew you a mystery; We shall not all sleep, but we shall all be changed, In a moment, in the twinkling of an eye, at the last trump: for the trumpet shall sound, and the dead shall be raised incorruptible, and we shall be changed. For this corruptible must put on incorruption, and this mortal must put on immortality' [1 Corinthians 15:51–53]. That's why God put an angel at the gate to the Garden of Eden, so fallen man would not eat of the tree of life and live forever."

Then Mara read Genesis 3:22–24. " 'And the Lord God said, Behold, the man is become as one of us, to know good and evil: and now, lest he put forth his hand, and take also of the tree of life, and eat, and live for ever: Therefore the Lord God sent him forth from the garden of Eden, to till the ground from whence he was taken. . . . and he placed at the east of the garden of Eden Cherubims, and a flaming sword which turned every way, to keep the way of the tree of life.' "

"I can see how it all fits together. Then what about hell?" The questions were tumbling out of Lila's mouth. "You said those who don't believe will perish. Don't bad people burn forever? Is hell burning now?" she asked.

"No, Lila. Everybody sleeps in the grave until Judgment Day. Then each gets his reward. God will rain fire on the wicked and burn them up. That's the purpose of the fire—not to torture them, but to end the curse of sin. God is love. The fire will finally burn up the devil and his evil angels and all sinners who followed them. It will cleanse the earth. Sin is like leprosy. The fire is called 'unquenchable' because nothing can put it out until it finishes its work and burns everything up that God wants burned. Then it will go out." Mara turned to Psalm 37:10, 11, 20. " 'For yet a little while, and the wicked shall not be; yea, thou shalt diligently consider his place, and it shall not be. But the meek shall inherit the earth; and shall delight themselves in the abundance of peace. . . . But the wicked shall perish, and the enemies of the Lord shall be as the fat of lambs: they shall consume away; into smoke shall they consume away.' You see," Mara concluded, "God will start all over again and make a whole new earth on this planet."

The women finally left; it seemed they had run out of questions at last. "Dear Lord, send Your Holy Spirit to make Your words clear in their minds," Mara prayed. "May they know You as a loving, merciful Savior and not as a cruel God."

Alone in the silent room now, Mara contemplated her life and the lonely days ahead. *Thank You, Lord,* she prayed in her heart, *for Ilija, my companion of more years than I can remember. You have kept my sons faithful. You have provided for my daughters. You have done wonders for me, O God. What changes You have wrought!* She recalled recent days. Ilija had worshiped with them Friday and Saturday evenings and sang their songs. Often he accompanied them to church. Johann joined the group in Uzveće. *Those words he spoke to me that Sunday long ago changed my life. Changed me, God, and changed many others.* As far as she knew, more than one hundred fifty people had believed the marvelous truths of the Bible due to her influence—truths forgotten over the years, replaced by men's ideas and traditions. *Wonderful God, how marvelous are all Your ways!*

One day not long afterwards, the incredible happened. Mladen's wife, Maria, came to see Mara, bearing great news. "Mara, see what the Lord has done!" she said ecstatically. "Mladen was baptized last Sabbath. Yes, Mara, it's true!"

"Mladen? Baptized?" Mara could hardly reply. "He tried to force me to give up my faith. He threatened to evict anyone in his family who believed differently. Now he's baptized? Miracle of miracles! How did it happen, Maria?"

"Well, when he learned that all six of our daughters had been baptized after me, I guess it was too much for him. He was greatly outnumbered!" Maria laughed. "Now, he's even talking about having church meetings in our home!"

"And Petar? What does he say?" Mara asked.

"Petar hasn't changed. He's still indifferent," Maria said. "Strange, isn't it, Mara? You never know who will respond to the Holy Spirit. No matter how stubborn or bad they may be, we must never give up."

"Everything will pass, and the Lord will come, Maria." Mara repeated the phrase familiar to all who knew her. "God calls everyone to come home to Him."

After Maria left, Mara picked up her Bible and read again the precious words that gave her hope:

And I saw a new heaven and a new earth: for the first heaven and the first earth were passed away; and there was no more sea. Then I John saw the holy city, new Jerusalem, coming down from God out of heaven, prepared as a bride adorned for her husband. And I heard a great voice out of heaven saying, Behold, the tabernacle of God is with men, and he will dwell with them, and they shall be his people, and God himself shall be with them, and be their God. And God shall wipe away all tears from their eyes; and there shall be no more death, neither sorrow, nor crying, neither shall there be any more pain: for the former things are passed away (Revelation 21:1–4).

"No more pain, no more sorrow, no more death, wars, or crying," she repeated. She quoted Psalm 30:5 from memory: " 'Weeping may endure for a night, but joy cometh in the morning.' Yes, Lord," she breathed, "joy on resurrection morning when I look in Your face and my loved ones are returned to me. 'Even so, come Lord Jesus' [Revelation 22:20]. Keep me faithful, Lord, until I say my last goodbye."

*Mara, flanked by her two
adult sons aged 22 years.*

*Mara and Ilija in his Austrian
tunic.*

Mara with her twins aged 11 and Tetka *Radosava (right) in Šabac when the boys first went away to school.*

Nata and her husband, Mića, and their son Jovica.

Leka and her husband, Živan, and two of their three sons, Jovan (left) and Pavle (right).

Vera and her husband, Duja.

The twins at age 17 with their sister Vera, age 19 years, in Šabac where the boys attended high school.

Voja (front row toward the right) sitting in the Belgrade church with members of his mandolin orchestra seated in rows on the left.

If you enjoyed this book, you'll enjoy these as well:

Red Star Rising
Sunshine Siu Stahl as told to Kay D. Rizzo. Shao Zhao Yang's extraordinary vocal talent propelled her to fame as an opera star in Communist China. Though she considered herself a Seventh-day Adventist Christian, on stage she could forget her Adventist upbringing and the public humiliation and persecution her family endured at the hands of Chairman Mao's Red Guards. The memories of her name change, family exile, and "denunciation meetings" made her grateful for her new life of stardom. But what of her faith? Could she ever really forget?
0-8163-2122-1. Paperback.
US$12.99, Can$17.99

Lotus Blossom Returns
Florence Nagel-Longway-Howlett with *Sandy Zaugg.*The remarkable story of a young missionary's determination to return to her beloved China—despite war, emergency plane landings, heartbreak, floods and seemingly "impossible" challenges.
0-8163-2044-6. Paperback.
US$14.99, Can$20.49.

Beyond the Veil of Darkness
Esmie G. Branner. **Beyond the Veil of Darkness** is an intimate first-person account of the struggles, opposition, and courageous triumph of a young Christian woman who clung to her faith in Jesus Christ despite the physical and mental abuse of a Muslim husband.
0-8163-1713-5. Paperback.
US$9.99, Can$13.49.

Order from your ABC by calling **1-800-765-6955**, or get online and shop our virtual store at **www.adventistbookcenter.com**.
- Read a chapter from your favorite book
- Order online
- Sign up for email notices on new products

Prices subject to change without notice.